A TRAVELER'S GUIDE TO THE HISTORY OF

BIOLOGY AND MEDICINE

by

Eric T. Pengelley
and
Daphne M. Pengelley

D1603158

The Trevor Hill Press

1986

To

David and Alison

May you travel and learn more than we have

THE AUTHORS

Eric T. Pengelley is Professor Emeritus at the University of California, Davis. He is a physiologist and historian of biology. His wife, Daphne, is an artist. He was born in Toronto, Canada, and she in Surrey, England. They have been married nearly 40 years, and live in Davis, California.

A TRAVELER'S GUIDE TO THE HISTORY OF
BIOLOGY AND MEDICINE

by

Eric T. Pengelley and Daphne M. Pengelley

Published and distributed by:

The Trevor Hill Press
P.O. Box 1851
Davis, California 95617-1851
U.S.A.

First Edition

Printed in the United States of America

Library of Congress Catalog Card Number 86-50325

ISBN 0-9616695-0-0

Cover design by Daphne Pengelley

ACKNOWLEDGEMENTS

We are both indebted to many people, historians, doctors, biologists, librarians, curators and others, all of whom (with one exception!) were more than helpful and cooperative. However, a few special thanks are necessary. Dr. Frederick F. Cartwright, the distinguished British anaesthetist and medical historian, has been a constant source of information and encouragement. His fund of knowledge is prodigious and he has always been willing to share it with us. Others who have given us major assistance and advice, include the late Miss Jessie Dobson of the Hunterian Museum, Royal College of Surgeons, London; Dr. William Bynum of the Wellcome Institute, London; Mr. Peter Gautrey of the Cambridge University Library, Cambridge, England; Dr. Maurice Fontaine and Dr. Francois Lachiver, both of the Musée National d'Histoire Naturelle, Paris; Dr. Ivan Assenmacher of the Université de Montpellier, Montpellier, France; Dr. Jurgens Aschoff and Dr. Eberhard Gwinner, both of the Max-Planck-Institut, Andechs, West Germany; Dr. Heinz Goerke of the Institut für Geschichte der Medizin, Munich, West Germany; Dr. Lorenzo Colombo of the Università di Padova, Padua, Italy; Dr. Bengt Johansson of the General Hospital, Malmö, Sweden; the late Dr. Charles Best of the Banting and Best Institute, Toronto, Canada; Dr. Audrey B. Davis of the National Museum of History and Technology, Washington, D.C.; and Dr. Ralph H. Kellogg of the University of California Medical School, San Francisco, California. We are also grateful to Mrs. Kathleen Green for her expert editing and proof reading. Finally, the senior author thanks the University of Califonia for granting him various leaves of absence to pursue the project.

CONTENTS

Introduction   1

1. **Britain**   3
    Aldershot   3
    Ardingly   6
    Ashford   8
    Berkeley   8
    Broadstone   12
    Cambridge   14
    Canterbury   22
    Downe   23
    East Kilbride   26
    East Wellow   28
    Edinburgh   29
    Folkestone   38
    Glasgow   41
    Gosport   48
    Hempstead   49
    Kew   50
    London   58
    Maer   88
    Middle Claydon   89
    Oxford   90
    Shrewsbury   94
    Teddington   95
    Tring   98
    Wisley   100
    York   101

2. **France**   102
    Arbois   103
    Beaune   107
    Dôle   108
    Montpellier   109
    Paris   114
    St. Julien-en-Beaujolais   136

3. **Federal Republic of Germany**   139
    Clausthal-Zellerfeld   139

		Frankfurt-am-Main	142
		Heidelberg	144
		Ingolstadt	146
		Kaiserswerth	147
		Marburg/Lahn	148
		Munich	151
		Neuss	153
		Remscheid-Lennep	155
		Würzburg	158
4.	**Italy**		160
		Florence	161
		Naples	166
		Padua	168
		Pisa	173
5.	**Switzerland**		177
		Basel	177
		Geneva	179
		Zürich	180
6.	**Austria**		183
		Vienna	183
7.	**Czechoslovakia**		188
		Brno	188
8.	**Hungary**		192
		Budapest	192
9.	**Holland**		195
		Leiden	195
10.	**Sweden**		199
		Lund	199
		Stenbrohult	200
		Uppsala	201
11.	**United States of America**		206
		Boston	206
		Cleveland	210
		Mackinac Island	211
		New York	213

Philadelphia	214
Washington	216
Willaimsburg	219
12. Canada	221
Toronto	221
Vancouver	225
Victoria	226
Index	227

INTRODUCTION

One of the greatest legacies of nations is the memory of their famous sons and daughters, and the inheritance of their great examples and achievements. The foregoing thought of Benjamin Disraeli nicely expresses the purpose of this book, which is to bring before the interested reader not only major people and events in the history of biology and medicine (commonly overlooked in general history and guide books), but also where to find the various places, buildings, artifacts and other memorabilia, associated with them. The scientific discoveries of these people have contributed enormously to our knowledge and understanding (both scientific and aesthetic) of the world, have enriched our cultural heritage, and made life more bearable on a day to day basis.

The idea for our work, and this resulting book , was based on the fact that very few people have much knowledge of biological and medical history, even less of their importance and significance, and less still of the places where the major events took place. This book, then, is both a historical guide and a geographical guide. The background work for this has taken several years, during which we traveled whenever time and money were available - - two things hard to come by! We have visited many of the countries of Western and Eastern Europe, as well as North America, where we studied, located, and photographed what is recorded in this book. Our task is of course far from complete, and indeed never will be, but we believe there is sufficient here to be of interest and value to many people. Inevitably we had to limit our historical time span which is from the beginning of the sixteenth century to the present.   In addition, we have chosen to describe only what we considered to be the most important people, events and places. This is arbitrary, but we did our best.

We were determined that none of what we described should be "secondhand." Thus almost everything that is described here has been visited and seen by one or other of us, but usually both. Any exceptions are duly noted.   The historical accounts are inevitably secondhand, though we have gone to great effort to make them as accurate as possible, but the actual places, buildings, equipment, books, etc., are all described from our own experiences. Of course time has passed since we began this project, and there will no doubt have been some changes, but we believe our accounts will serve as an accurate guide. Our descriptions include not just places associated with specific people, but important libraries, laboratories, botanical gardens, universities, museums, etc., which have played a large part in the advance of biological and medical knowledge.

In addition to actually locating the various places of interest, we have, in almost all cases, included specific instructions of how to get there by various means of transportation. Unfortunately wrong information on this is abundant, as we have often found to our sorrow! We have given the most direct and/or main route, but there are usually many others, often much more pleasant and interesting. Main roads are all too commonly crowded with heavy trucks and not that easy to drive on. This is particularly true for the countries of Western Europe. If time is not of primary concern, our advice would be to get off the main roads.

Where possible we have included information on "times of opening " of the various buildings, museums, etc. We must stress, however, that the times we give were those in effect when we were there. As every traveler knows such things can change rapidly, and it is essential, therefore, to enquire about opening times well in advance if disappointments are to be avoided. Furthermore, some of the places we describe are not open to the public on a regular basis, and special permission to see them must be made in advance. This can however, usually be obtained by really interested people. At each location we give as much information as possible about this, but one should always respect the institutions' privacy, rules and wishes in this regard.

The book is arranged country by country, and within each country the places of biological and medical interest are listed in alphabetical order. Under these, the events and their surviving historical associations are described, including, where appropriate, short histories of specific people. However, there is extensive cross referencing, because of course people and events have seldom been isolated to one place.

It is with pleasure therefore, that we send you forth on a historical and geographical "trail of discovery" in biology and medicine. We hope you enjoy it as much as we have.

Chapter 1

BRITAIN

Britain has a long and distinguished history in many areas of human endeavour, but none is more impressive than their achievements in science. From the basic sciences in general the names of Roger Bacon (1214-1294), Robert Boyle (1627-1691), Sir Isaac Newton (1642-1727), John Dalton (1766-1844), Michael Faraday (1791-1867), and Lord Kelvin (1824-1907) rank among the greats of all time. It is no less the case in the fields of biology and medicine, where we will have much to say about people such as William Harvey (1578-1657), Stephen Hales (1677-1761), William (1718-1783) and John (1728-1793) Hunter, Edward Jenner (1749-1823), Sir William Hooker (1785-1865), Sir James Young Simpson (1811-1870), Charles Darwin (1809-1882), Sir Joseph Dalton Hooker (1817-1912), Joseph Lord Lister (1827-1912), and many more.

The places associated with these men and women are inevitably scattered, and many more historical associations survive of some than of others. In recent British history there have been two events in which great physical destruction took place. The first of these was their Civil War in the first half of the seventeenth century, and the second was in World War II (1939-1945). Regrettably the history of biology and medicine did not escape these two disasters, and in addition time and change have taken their toll. We must also note that it is only in very recent times that it was even thought desirable to preserve scientific monuments. Nevertheless Britain is very richly endowed with such monuments.

Roads in Britain are generally good, and British Rail offers excellent service to most places. There are also many bus services. All road directions we give are from London, unless otherwise noted.

ALDERSHOT (Hampshire)
Location - 35 miles southwest of London
Train - From London (Waterloo).

Road - Take the M3 or A30 towards Basingstoke. Near Camberley
        turn off along the A321 to Aldershot.

Aldershot is the "military town" of England, where soldiers
have been trained for over a century. However there are also three
excellent historical museums: dental, medical and nursing.

Royal Army Dental Corps Museum
H.Q. and Training Centre
Royal Army Dental Corps
Queens Avenue
Aldershot.

Phone - (0252) - 24431 and ask for the Royal Army Dental Corps
        Training Center.
Opening hours:
        Upon request at the main desk of the training center.
        No charge for admission.

Fortunately the founders of this museum concentrated on
dental history rather than military history, and the layout of the
museum is chronological starting about 1660 and continuing to the
present day. The whole museum is a remarkable documentary
display of the advance of dentistry for over 300 years. Some of it is
pretty grim! In addition to the various, and very interesting,
instruments, apparatus, etc., the visitor is reminded of the many
problems and events which have affected dentistry directly and
indirectly. For example as early as the 17th century, military
surgeons were required to preserve the soldiers' front teeth so that
they could bite through the cartridge when loading their flintlock
muskets. With the advance of weaponry, and biting through the
cartridge no longer necessary, the surgeon specialized in the
preservation of the molars so that the soldiers could chew their food
properly, and the front teeth were no longer considered essential!
Vivid displays depict jaw and facial wounds so common in war
(particularly in WW I with its trench warfare), and these involved the
dentist in their repair. Quite contrary to popular belief, some
remarkable "plastic surgery" was done in WWI, rather than having to
wait for WWII, and much of this was done by surgeons and dentists
working together. The leader in this area was the New Zealander,
Sir Harold Delf Gillies (1882-1960). Of great interest also is a
comparison of field dental units of WWII from the British, American
and German armies. One is struck at once by the enormous

4

technical superiority of the German unit. In our opinion this museum is a "little gem."

Royal Army   Medical Corps Historical Museum
Keogh Barracks
Ash Vale
Near Aldershot.

Phone- (0252) - 24431, Ext. Keogh 212
Opening Hours:
>   Monday - Friday, 9.00 - 16.00
>   Weekends - By appointment.
>   No charge for admission.

One of the earliest recorded references to army medical doctors is found in the Greek poet Homer's account of the siege of Troy (1190 BC), and certainly from that time onwards almost all armies have supplied some kind of medical care for their soldiers. This museum displays the development of that care, and consequently is of great interest for the history of medicine in general.

The museum is relatively new, having been opened in 1981, but it is based on a much older one. Fortunately it is being kept up to date under the able leadership of Lt. Colonel Roy Eyeions, who is the curator (1986), and there are even plans for expansion.

The displays are a blend of medical and military history, and are arranged chronologically in ten sections. The first section is from the earliest times to 1660, and the last from 1945 to the present. Some of the displays are very realistic and there is no attempt to hide the horrors of war, but great emphasis is placed on what the medical services can do to alleviate suffering. Some of the more spectacular items on view include the following: Hanoverian Army medical instruments from 1715, Napoleon's dental instruments, water color drawings of the wounded at Waterloo (1815), a bullet extractor using electricity for detection, branding instruments used on deserters, iron lungs, mobile field anaesthesia apparatus and a mobile surgery table with a mock casualty. All in all an important museum in the history of medicine, and a good place to learn the important contributions made to medicine under the pressures of war.

Queen Alexandra's Royal Army Nursing Corps
Training Center
Nursing Museum
Farnborough Road
Aldershot.

Phone - (0252) - 24431, Ext. 315 or 301
Opening hours:
>   By appointment only, and it is necessary to phone in
>   advance.
>   No charge for admission.

Within this training center for army nurses is a small museum devoted to the history of army nursing, and in fact it supplies a history of nursing in general. A small pamphlet, as a guide, is available, and an excellent history of Queen Alexandra's Royal Army Nursing Corps may be bought, and we recommend this.

This museum is a blend of military and nursing history, and tends to be photographic except for the displays of nurses' uniforms. However, they have various artifacts of the nursing profession and some priceless objects such as the carriage used by Florence Nightingale (see under East Wellow, Middle Claydon and London, St. Thomas' Hospital) in the Crimea. The displays are arranged chronologically, and at present the museum is being redesigned and will in due course exhibit many new items from their undisplayed collections. This is the only Nursing Museum we are aware of, and is well worth a visit.

Before leaving Aldershot, the visitor will no doubt wish to see many other things there of historical interest. These are explained in a pamphlet entitled " Aldershot Military Town Trail," which contains directions for seeing such diverse items as a Dakota preserved from WWII and a military horse cemetery!

ARDINGLY (Sussex)
Location - 35 miles South of London.
Train - From London (Victoria) to Haywards Heath, and then by bus
       or taxi to Ardingly.

Road - Take the A23 going south from central London and join the M23 towards Brighton. Just past Crawley join the A23 again as far as Handcross. Then turn left (east) onto B2110 towards Balcombe, and follow this across the reservoir. At Ardingly turn left (north) onto B2028 to Wakehurst Place Gardens.

Wakehurst Place Gardens
Ardingly.

Opening hours:
>Summer daily 10.00-19.00
>Winter daily 10.00- 16.00
>Small charge for admission.

Wakehurst Place is a National Trust property leased to the Ministry of Agriculture, Fisheries and Food as an addition to the Royal Botanic Gardens at Kew (see under Kew). This supplies Kew with a much greater variety of growing conditions for various plants, and much larger facilities for botanic research. The gardens consist of 462 acres, most of which is natural woodland, in which the visitor can roam freely. This is an ideal place to see various species of trees, shrubs, etc., and their ecology in the natural woodlands of the area. Also there are extensive formal gardens, where there are large numbers of imported species- - all beautifully maintained.

It is here at Wakehurst that the Royal Botanic Gardens perform all their plant physiological research. They are particularly concerned with the physiology of seeds, seed germination and storage. They maintain a seed bank for many different types of people, including conservationists. They are concerned to find out how long various seeds can be stored and still remain viable. There is enormous variation between species, but most can probably be stored from 50-100 years.

Inscribed on the sundial within the gardens are the following lines by the American poet John Whittier (1807-1892), which expresses the attitude of those who love plants:

>Give fools their gold and knaves their power
>Let fortune's bubbles rise and fall
>Who sows a field, or trains a flower,
>Or plants a tree, is more than all.

Although the primary function of Wakehurst Place is scientific botany, it is also a very beautiful place and should not be missed.

ASHFORD (Kent)
Location - 50 miles southeast of London.
Train - From London (Charing Cross).
Road - Take the A20 to the south, and follow this (or the M20)
      through Maidstone to Ashford.

Ashford, Kent, is not known to have been directly associated with William Harvey (see also under Folkestone, Canterbury and Hempstead), the man who discovered and proved the phenomenon of blood circulation. But the county of Kent is "Harvey Country," so to speak, for it was here that he was born and brought up, and there are two things in Ashford which commemorate the memory of this giant of medicine.

Willesborough is a suburb of Ashford, which has a nice pub called "The William Harvey." However, more important is the fact that in the garden of the pub there is a fine statue of William Harvey. It has an interesting history. About 160 years ago it was sculptured by Henry Weekes, and stood outside the Royal College of Physicians in London. During WWII the college was badly bombed and the statue damaged. While the debris was being cleaned up, and in some way, no one knows how, the statue found its way to the garden of this pub where it is today! It is well looked after and interesting to see. Also in Willesborough is the new William Harvey Hospital and outside the main entrance is a copy of the William Harvey statue at Folkestone. It is very impressive.

BERKELEY (Gloucestershire)
Location - 105 miles west of London and 12 miles south of
          Gloucester.
Train - From London (Paddington) to Gloucester, and then by bus or
        taxi to Berkeley.
Road -Take the M4 to the west as far as exit 20 (which is where it
       crosses the M5). Take the M5 north to exit 14 and then join
       the A38 north to Stone. At Stone take the B4509 (left) to
       Berkeley.

Berkeley (pronounced Barkeley) will remain celebrated for all time as the birthplace and home of one of mankind's greatest benefactors, Edward Jenner (1749-1823), whose monumental work first brought under control the dread disease of smallpox, and which it would now appear has been eradicated from the earth - - we may hope forever.

The Jenner Museum
The Chantry
Church Lane
Berkeley, Gloucestershire.

Phone - (0453) - 810631
Opening hours:
     April 1 - September 30, every day, 11.00 - 17.30
     October - Sundays only, 11.00 - 17.30
     Closed November - March
     Small charge for admission.

     In a world now devoid of this disease it is really very difficult for us to understand the terrible scourge of smallpox. It was highly contagious, and many a doctor contracted it while trying to treat a patient. It killed thousands (particularly children) and left other thousands visibly and badly scarred for life. The disease was probably of eastern origin and was brought to Europe by returning crusaders in the 11th and 12th centuries. From there, in due course, it spread throughout the world. It was a major factor in the virtual extermination of the North American Indian.
     Edward Jenner was born in Berkeley, where his father was vicar, but at the age of five both his mother and father died leaving him an orphan under the care of his elder brother Stephen, another clergyman. At the early age of twelve Edward was apprenticed to a surgeon, David Ludlow, under whom he worked for nine years. Then at the age of twenty-one he went to London to study anatomy and surgery under the most famous doctor of his day, John Hunter (see under London and East Kilbride) with whom he corresponded until the latter's death in 1793. In 1773 Jenner returned to Berkeley, established himself in medical practice there, and in due course married Catherine Kingscote. Upon marriage they moved into Chantry Cottage, where they lived (with only short absences) for the rest of their lives.
     Jenner, following the accepted practice of his day, inoculated many of his patients against smallpox (using fluid from a smallpox pustule) but soon found that some patients were resistant to the disease, and learned further that these patients had apparently all had a disease contracted from cows, known as cowpox. This is a relatively rare and mild disease, though prevalent in Western

9

England at the time, and Jenner found that amongst milkmaids and others having close contact with cows, it was generally believed that contraction of cowpox gave protection, if not complete immunity, against smallpox. Thus it occurred to Jenner that if patients were inoculated with the fluid of a pustule of cowpox, from which they would contract cowpox (hopefully in mild form), that this might confer immunity to smallpox. Furthermore, and most important, Jenner hoped to create a reservoir of cowpox by transferring the disease via inoculation from human to human. This indeed proved possible, and it also proved possible to artificially store and ship the fluid obtained from a pustule of cowpox.

Jenner was reluctant to try the crucial experiment, but finally on May 14,1796 (perhaps remembering the famous advice of his former teacher , John Hunter, "But why think? Why not try the experiment?"), Jenner inoculated an eight year old boy, James Phipps, with the fluid from a cowpox pustule obtained from a milkmaid who had the disease. James contracted cowpox, but recovered within a few days. Then on July 1, the same year, Jenner inoculated him with smallpox and to everyone's delight, the boy did not contract smallpox.

Jenner understood the importance and potential of his discovery, and in the following year, 1797, he sent a short paper on the subject to the President (Sir Joseph Banks) of the Royal Society. His paper was rejected! However in 1798 he published, at his own expense, a short book describing the nature of cowpox and the immunity (not permanent) it confers against smallpox. The book was entitled: " An inquiry into the Causes and Effects of Variolae Vaccinae, a disease discovered in some of the Western Counties of England particularly Gloucestershire, and known by the name of Cowpox." It was the result of enormous perseverance and careful reasoning, and is one of the great works in medical history. With its publication Jenner may be considered the founder of immunology with all the blessings which since have followed from it. He also coined the word virus (Latin = poison or slimy liquid). The process of inoculation with cowpox quickly became known as vaccination (Latin: vacca = cow), and soon spread far and wide.

Mary, Countess of Berkeley (1767-1844), a very influential local woman, persuaded Jenner to vaccinate her large family of children, and through her Jenner also vaccinated the royal children of George III. This helped enormously to spread and popularize vaccination. By 1801 it was being used extensively in the Persian Gulf and India, and Jenner personally sent vaccine to President

Thomas Jefferson of the United States, who vaccinated his family and friends at Monticello.

Fame, honors, but little fortune were poured upon Edward Jenner after his discovery. Yet it is nice to record that despite this he remained a simple country doctor in his native Berkeley. The British Parliament voted him a grant of money, which made life easier for him, and in 1804, although Britain and France were at war, Napoleon Bonaparte had a medal struck in his honor, and in 1805 made vaccination compulsory in the French Army. Also at Jenner's personal request Napoleon released some British prisoners, and in so doing is said to have remarked: "We can refuse nothing to that man." Such was Jenner's prestige.

Jenner's wife, Catherine, died in 1815, and he later died of a stroke in 1823. Despite the fact that he could have been buried in Westminster Abbey, he preferred Berkeley Church where his body lies today.

The Chantry (formerly Edward Jenner's house) was bought by the Jenner Trust and the British Society of Immunology, and opened as the Jenner Museum in May 1985. There was previously a small museum in a little house on Church Lane.

The rooms comprising the museum are as follows:

1. Entrance Hall, with various items for sale and pictures depicting various events in Jenner's life.
2. The Jenner Room, with cases of articles belonging to Jenner, including some of his instruments, manuscripts, photographs, paintings, prints, publications, family letters and his original handwritten will of 34 pages.
3. The Smallpox Vaccination Room, with pictures of people with cowpox and smallpox, cases of instruments used in vaccination, and cases of honors bestowed on Jenner.
4. The Study. Jenner's original study, with his furniture, instruments, books,etc., all beautifully restored and displayed behind glass.
5. The WHO room. The World Health Organization Room, with displays depicting the work of WHO.
6. The Immunology Room, showing the history of immunology from a historical perspective.
7. There are also administrative offices and a conference room.

Adjacent to the Chantry is the Jenner Hut or Temple of Vaccinia, where Jenner vaccinated the poor from far and wide, and also the village church where he and his immediate family are buried. His grave is near the altar. Jenner was born in what is now the town post office.

No visitor to Berkeley will want to miss Berkeley Castle, which adjoins the churchyard on the outskirts of the town. This is the private residence of the Berkeley family, but is periodically open to the public by the Berkeleys' permission. Incidentally the Berkeley family goes back 800 years in a direct male line! Of great interest also is that the Berkeley family has always been concerned with the support of potentially great men and their achievements, for not only did they sponsor Edward Jenner, but William Harvey as well. Of further interest is the fact that it was a member of the Berkeley family who gave his library to start the now famous University of California at Berkeley.

In addition to all these interesting things to see at Berkeley, we would recommend that visitors also take the opportunity to see the magnificent Jenner statue in Gloucester Cathedral, and the nearby and fascinating Wildfowl Trust at Slimbridge.

BROADSTONE (Dorset)

Location - 110 miles southwest of London, near Bournemouth.
Train - From London(Waterloo) to Bournemouth, then by taxi to Broadstone.
Road - From London take the M3 or the A30 to beyond Basingstoke, and fork onto the A33 to Winchester. Follow the A33 around Winchester and then fork on to the M27 towards Cadnam. At Cadnam join the A31 to Ringwood and Wimborne Minster. At Wimborne Minster take the A349 towards Poole, but before reaching Poole take the small marked road to Broadstone.

Broadstone Cemetery
Broadstone.

Opening hours:
Daily 9.00 - dusk.

Broadstone Cemetery is the final resting place of the great biologist and explorer Alfred Russel Wallace (1823-1913). Wallace died in a house he owned nearby, but it has now been completely demolished.

Alfred Russel Wallace was born in Usk, Monmouthshire, on the north side of the Severn in Wales. (The house in which he was born still stands, but it is privately occupied.) His family suffered periodic economic setbacks, but he appears to have had a happy childhood though a minimum of formal schooling. Wallace is an excellent example of a self-educated man. He never attended university, but by wide reading from the earliest age onwards he became a very knowledgeable person. For several years he worked with his brother, William, as a surveyor, but in 1848, at the age of 25, he set out on the first of his many travels to far away lands. From 1848-1852, he explored the Amazon basin, and collected and studied prodigious amounts of natural material which he took with him on the return voyage to England. However, disaster overtook the ship on which he was traveling. It caught fire and sank, and Wallace barely escaped with his life. All of his specimens were lost. Despite this, in the following year, 1853, he published his fascinating book "A Narrative of Travels on the Amazon and Rio Negro." The evidence is clear that from this time, perhaps before, Wallace was interested in organic evolution, and the mechanism of "speciation." In 1854 Wallace set out for the Malay Archipelago, and for the next 8 years he explored and collected in the general region of what is now known as Indonesia. One of his specific aims was to study the geographical distribution of animals, with the hope of uncovering their evolutionary origins. He was eminently successful in his quest! In 1858, while Charles Darwin (see under Downe) was at work on his book, which was eventually to become "The Origin of Species by Means of Natural Selection," Wallace wrote to Darwin and expressed very similar theories as a result of his work in Malay and Indonesia. This led to the publication of a joint paper by Darwin and Wallace, and thus Wallace may rightly be described as the codiscoverer of evolution by natural selection. However, it was left to Darwin to put the theory forth in understandable terms, to document it with his overwhelming amount of evidence, and to explain its scientific implications. In 1862 Wallace returned to England, hailed as a great naturalist, and rightly so. In 1869 his experiences in Malay were put forth in his book "The Malay Archipelago: The Land of the Orang-Utan, and the Bird of Paradise. A Narrative of Travel with Studies of Man and Nature." It is one of the best natural history books ever written. More important still, from a scientific point of view, was his work "The Geographical Distribution of Animals" (1876). With this he founded the science of animal geography and it is still read by professional students of the subject today. It explains the mechanisms, on a worldwide basis, by which animals have evolved in their present habitats. Wallace wrote a great deal more in his long life of 90 years, and in some of these his curious religious views are intermingled with his scientific thought. But it is for those works already mentioned, and his great theory of evolution by natural selection, that he will be remembered as a naturalist and scientist of the highest rank.

To find Wallace's grave in Broadstone Cemetery, enter by the main gate and follow down the walkway. Less than 100 yards on the right, and near the walkway, you will see a large simulated tree trunk on top of his grave. He and his wife, Annie, are buried side by side here, and there are two simple plaques on the tomb giving their names, birth and death dates. It is a pleasant thought that the great, and widely traveled naturalist lies in such a beautiful place.

CAMBRIDGE (Cambridgeshire)
Location - 55 miles north of London.
Train - From London (Liverpool Street).
Road - Take the A11 which leads into the M11 at Wanstead. Follow the M11 until it again joins the A11 near Bishop's Stortford. Continue on the A11 until just beyond Great Chesterford, then take the left fork onto the A130, which leads via A10 into Cambridge.

The history of Cambridge goes back to Roman times, when there was a Roman camp. However, when the Domesday Book was compiled 1000 years later in 1086 AD, there were still only 400 houses in Cambridge. Today its fame rests on its university, one of the truly great educational centres of the world. It is younger than Oxford, and it is probable that its history as a "community of scholars" goes back to 1209, when some scholars from Oxford settled there after being forced to leave Oxford because of "trouble with the townspeople"! But by the middle of the century it could rightly claim to be a university. In 1284 the university's first college, Peterhouse, was founded, and many more have been founded over the centuries. At present there are 31 different colleges.

The university is basically a federal structure, in which the colleges are semi-autonomous, and all students must belong to a college. However it is the university which imposes minimum entrance requirements, is responsible for formal instruction, conducts examinations, and confers degrees.

Cambridge is an exciting, dynamic, and very pleasant place, and for "first-time" visitors we cannot recommend too strongly that as soon as possible they visit the Tourist Information Centre. It is in Wheeler Street, an extension of Benet Street, which in turn runs off

King's Parade. It is open Monday-Friday 9.30-17.30, Saturdays 9.00-17.00, closed Sundays. Not only is the Information Centre a mine of information on all things the visitor needs, but in addition it conducts guided "Walking Tours of the Colleges." These are normally at 11.00 and 14.00, Monday-Saturday, and last about 1 1/2 hours. They are popular and limited to 20 persons each. Thus it is best to buy your ticket well in advance if possible. This tour will give you a marvelous introduction and orientation to Cambridge and its university. One of the many nice things about Cambridge is that it is still small enough, and concentrated enough, that virtually everything the visitor may want to see can be reached on foot, and that is certainly the way to see it. The main life of the city is on either side of the central street of St. Johns- - Trinity- - King's Parade- - Trumpington.

In contrast to Oxford University, Cambridge has always encouraged the sciences, and has produced such men as William Harvey, Sir Isaac Newton, Stephen Hales, Charles Darwin and Francis Crick, all of whom had an enormous impact on the development of biology and medicine. Within the various colleges, laboratories, museums, etc., science has flourished, and the visitor to Cambridge can see some of the places associated with the great development of biology which has taken place there. We must stress however, that Cambridge University and its colleges are active educational and research institutions, and the visitor should respect this fact and not expect to be able to see everything on demand. The porters' offices at the entrance to colleges, are however generally cooperative, and will tell you what is open to the public and what is not.

Gonville and Caius College
Trinity Street.

It was here that William Harvey was a student between 1593-1599. His life, discoveries and work are described under Folkestone. It is regrettable however, that virtually nothing survives at the college that is known to have been associated with Harvey. It is not even known which rooms he occupied, but nevertheless it is exciting to realize that Harvey once walked the courtyards and corridors of this college. There is a so-called "Harvey Court," but it is modern and simply named in Harvey's honor. Of particular interest is their magnificent historical library with a fine collection of 16th and 17th century medical works from Padua, and there is little doubt that Harvey was aware of these, which in due course led him to study at

Padua, then the foremost medical school in the world. The college library is not open to the public, but one may request to see it.

Trinity College
Trinity Street.

This was the college of Sir Isaac Newton who was a student here between 1661-1665. However, he stayed on at Cambridge as a professor until 1701. Newton was of course not principally famous for biological discoveries, but his work in physics and mathematics was so great that it influenced all science, and it would be inappropriate to ignore him while we are describing historical scientific associations in Cambridge. The rooms that Newton occupied, while at Trinity College, are known. They are at ground level and the exterior aspect is usually pointed out by the guide in one of the "Walking Tours of the Colleges." Of further interest is the fact that in the entrance hall of the Trinity College Chapel (usually open) there is a magnificent statue of Newton as a young man.

Corpus Christi College
Trumpington Street.

This is where Stephen Hales was a student. He is often referred to as the founder of plant physiology. His work is described under Teddington. Stephen Hales' days as a student at Corpus Christi were from 1696-1700, but like Newton he stayed on at Cambridge, in his case until 1709. The only part of the College that survives from Hales' days is the Old Court, which dates from 1350. The rest of the college is later than the 17th century. Stephen Hales unquestionably occupied rooms somewhere around the Old Court, but it is not known which ones. The Old Court can be found through an archway to the left of the present Main Court. For those with more than passing interest in Stephen Hales, it is possible to purchase (for £1) at the college office an excellent biography of him by the late Dr. A.E. Clark-Kennedy.

Christ's College
St. Andrews Street

This was the college of Charles Darwin. His life and work are described under Downe. Darwin was a student at Christ's from 1827-1831, and his major field of study was theology. However, it was during his days here that his biological interests were established, mainly due to the influence of Professor John Stevens Henslow (1796-1861), a very distinguished botanist, with whom he became a close friend. The rooms Darwin occupied while at Christ's are known. They are off the main quad to the right, up a small flight of stairs, and they are referred to as G4. One may see the location, but the rooms are privately occupied. In the main dining room, which can usually be seen if not in actual use, is a magnificent portrait of Darwin by W.W. Ouless, alongside other portraits of Christ's distinguished graduates, including John Milton (1608-1674). Of importance also at Christ's is their superb historical library, which is the same library Darwin knew and used. They have, among other things, over 100 letters, written by Darwin while he was a student at Christ's. The library is not open to the public, but permission to see it can be requested.

Darwin College
Silver Street.

This college is of recent origin and is located in a lovely old house which belonged to one of the sons of Charles Darwin. Of great interest is the fact that it was here that Gwen Raverat (née Darwin, and Charles' granddaughter) was brought up, and it was the setting for her classic work "Period Piece."

Department of Zoology and Museum
Pembroke Street.

Opening hours:
> Museum: Monday - Friday only, 14.15-16.45.
> Children must be accompanied by an adult.
> No charge for admission.

The department has had a long and distinguished history in the development of modern zoology. It is a research and teaching department, but they have a very fine Museum of Zoology as well. It is not intended as a Natural History Museum. All the main groups of animals are arranged systematically, and it emphasizes taxonomy, anatomy and ecology. It is very modern, and the exhibits superbly displayed. The curator is Mr. R. D. Norman, and if he is not busy (unlikely!), you may ask to see some of their very special collections, which include fish and birds (including some Galapagos Finches) collected by Charles Darwin. They also have slides of the appendages of Darwin's famous collection of barnacles, which he used as the basic material for his two volumes on living barnacles, and two on fossil barnacles. The zoological museum is a fascinating place for those with an interest in biology and its history.

The Botany Department
Downing Street.
Opening hours:
>Normal academic hours.
>No charge for admission.

Historically this may be described as one of the homes of modern botany, for it is here for over two hundred years that botany has been pursued as a science rather than simply as an aid to medicine or as horticulture. This is an active department of teaching and research, but the visitor may ask to see their superb botanic library, and above all their unique herbarium. Within this herbarium are the Galapagos plant specimens collected 150 years ago by Charles Darwin himself, and which played such a large role in helping him to unravel his theories on evolution. The "line of descent," so to speak, for this collection was from Darwin to Professor John Henslow, to Sir Joseph Dalton Hooker (see under Kew) to the Botany Department. Amazingly enough the collection is still not yet fully studied and documented. Within the library are some very fine busts of famous botanists which the visitor can see.

The Old Cavendish Laboratory
Free School Lane.

It was here between 1951 and 1953 that Francis Crick and James Watson unravelled the structure of deoxyribose nucleic acid (DNA), the basic material of life, and this was certainly the most important biological discovery of this century. In addition to Crick and Watson, Ernest Rutherford, J.J. Thomson and James Clerk Maxwell all worked within the walls of the Old Cavendish Laboratory. Crick and Watson actually worked in the Austin Wing (clearly marked), and on the wall outside the main entrance is a plaque commemorating the distinguished scientific history of the institute. Of interest also is the little house where Francis Crick lived while working on the structure of DNA. It is at 19-20 Portugal Place, and has a "golden helix" hung above the front door! It is a private residence but visitors can see the outside.

Francis Crick was born in Northampton in 1916 of middle class business-minded parents, and he was the only member of the family to exhibit an interest and indeed passion for science. In due course (1937) he received a B.Sc. degree in physics from University College, London, and afterwards worked as a research student until the coming of World War II in 1939 when he became a physicist with the British Admiralty. It was here in the Mine Design Department that he demonstrated his ability to go straight to the central core of a particular problem. However it was not until 1947 that he went to Cambridge and turned his attention to biology, as distinct from physics. He joined the Cavendish Laboratory and was admitted as a Ph.D. student, in 1949, working on x-ray diffraction of protein. Here in 1951 he became associated with a young visiting American biologist, James Watson, and together for two years they worked "on and off" on the structure of DNA. They were successful beyond their wildest dreams. James Dewey Watson's career, up to this time, had been less spectacular than Crick's, but he was regarded as a very able young biologist. Born in Chicago in 1928, he received, in due course, his B.S. from the University of Chicago, and his Ph.D. from the University of Indiana, and at the time he met and worked with Crick he was a "visiting fellow" in various places in Europe.

On April 25, 1953, Crick and Watson published in the British journal Nature, their classic one page article "Molecular Structure of Nucleic Acids." In it they gave a diagram of what has become famous as the "double helix," and in addition made a superb understatement, "It has not escaped our notice that the specific pairing we have postulated immediately suggests a possible copying mechanism for the genetic material." Their theoretical structure and postulation proved to be correct, and with it a new era of genetic and molecular research, with all its implications, was ushered in. In 1962, Crick and Watson were awarded the Nobel Prize for their work, but it is important to point out that their achievements did not occur "in vacuo," for the Nobel Prize also went to Maurice Wilkins, John Kendrew and Max Perutz, all of whom contributed to this discovery. Many people have regretted that the prize was not also awarded to their co-worker, Rosalind Franklin, who died so tragically soon after this great event. Francis Crick and James Watson have both gone on to distinguished biological careers.

The Whipple Museum of the History of Science
Free School Lane.

Opening hours:
    Monday - Friday 14.00 - 16.00
    No charge for admission.

This is part of the University's Department of the History and
Philosophy of Science. Here in this museum are superb historical
collections of microscopes, telescopes, mathematical instruments
and apparatus of great variety, much of it used directly in medicine.
There is also a library devoted to the history of science.

The University Botanic Garden
Bateman Street.

Opening hours:
    Monday - Saturday 8.00- 17.00
    No charge for admission.

This botanic garden is under the direction of the botany
department. Its main functions are research and education, as has
been the case since its inception, but it is a very beautiful place as
well, and a haven of peace and quiet- - reinforced by the signs which
read "no dogs, no games, no bicycles, no transistors"! Founded in
1760, it moved to its present site of 40 acres in 1831. At this time
Professor John Stevens Henslow (see previously) was Professor of
Botany. He was a very dynamic and farsighted young man, and set
the tone for the whole development of the garden, which still goes
on today. The research function of the garden has tended to
concentrate on taxonomy, but much plant genetic work has also
been done there, including that of Sir William Bateson. In recent
years the research function has increased, and they also train very
high quality horticulturalists. In addition to the many special gardens
and glass houses, there is a systematic garden with over 80 families
of plants represented, and the trees surrounding the outer edge of
the eastern half are planted in taxonomic groupings. A systematic
garden is one in which the plants are placed and grown in their
natural and evolutionary relationships. Being primarily a research
botanic garden, it naturally has an extensive library which is
particularly strong in the history of horticulture of the 17th and 18th
centuries. There are also many unique and valuable general
holdings going back to pre-Linnean times. There is also an

extensive collection of botanical serials, monographs, maps, etc., some extinct journals and very interesting floras. All in all the University Botanic Garden is one of the best and most distinguished in the world, and continues to play a large role in the development of scientific botany.

The Cambridge University Main Library
West Road.

Opening hours:
>Not open to the public except by special permission, but from Monday - Friday at 15.00 the public can be shown around the library.

This is a vast modern complex dating from 1934. It was designed by the architect Sir Gilbert Scott. However, the origins of the University Library go back to the 14th century, and it was well established by the beginning of the 15th century. Since then it has had a checkered history, but today is certainly one of the great libraries of the world, and is particularly strong in the natural sciences. It is one of five copyright libraries in Britain, and as such is entitled to a free copy of every book published in Britain. Its historical collections in the natural sciences are probably unrivaled anywhere. A very interesting historical sketch booklet of the library is available, and for lovers of biology there is also published a "Handlist of Darwin Papers" in the possession of the library. The university library is the main depository for the Darwinian papers and books. Some of these are at times on special display, but normally are not available to the public except by special permission for scholarly purposes. The Cambridge University Library played, and continues to play, a huge role in the ongoing development of the science of biology.

Fitzwilliam Museum
Trumpington Street.

Opening hours:
>Tuesday - Saturday 10.00-17.00
>Sunday 14.15 - 17.00
>Closed Monday.
>Small charge for admission.

In addition to the foregoing places of biological interest, no visitor to Cambridge will want to miss the Fitzwilliam Museum. Unfortunately this marvelous museum is having such financial troubles that they have had to close some of the galleries on alternate days - - very distressing for the short term visitor. This is not a museum of science, but a great art and antiquities museum.

CANTERBURY (Kent)
Location - 55 miles southeast of London.
Train - From London (Victoria) direct.
Road - Pick up the A2 at Greenwich and follow this southeast
        through Rochester, Gillingham, Sittingborne and on to
        Canterbury.

Canterbury, Kent, is famous for its Cathedral, and the fact that it is considered "the home" of Protestant religions. However Canterbury has another claim to fame, namely that William Harvey (see also under Ashford, Folkestone and Hempstead) attended the King's School as a young student. The King's School adjoins the Cathedral and is closely associated with it.

King's School
Canterbury

The King's School is a choir school, whose origins are lost in antiquity but certainly go back well over 1000 years. The main entrance to the school is through the 13th century gate off Broad Street, which leads into the Green Court, and the buildings of the school surround this. There are many other walking entrances, including some from the gardens of the Cathedral. There is an even older entrance gate dating from the 11th century, but it is now bricked over, though still easily seen.

In 1588, at the age of 10, Harvey entered the King's School, and remained there for 5 years. He was not a King's scholar, but a day pupil, and probably lived in Hawks Lane, which still survives, though the actual house he lived in is not known. All the memorabilia associated with Harvey which the school possessed have been scattered since Harvey was there. However, it is a fascinating place to visit and realize that William Harvey studied and walked in these same buildings and grounds four centuries ago. He is by far their most distinguished pupil! Of course the visitor to King's School will also wish to see the adjoining Cathedral, which is the seat of the Archbishop of Canterbury and has a very long and interesting history.

DOWNE (Kent)
Location - 15 miles south of London.
Train - From London (Victoria) to Bromley South, then by taxi or bus #146 (infrequent) to the village of Downe.
Road - From London, take the A21 south at Lewisham and follow this through Bromley and on to Bromley Common (near Hayes) and then take the right fork onto the A233. Follow this for about 2 miles where there is a left turn on a small country road to the village of Downe.

Here in this village at Down House, Charles Darwin (1809-1882) lived and worked for the last 40 years of his life. The house is now a museum and is owned and operated by The Royal College of Surgeons.

Down House
Luxted Road
Downe.

Phone - Farnborough 59119
Opening hours:
    Daily 13.00 - 18.00
    Closed Monday and Friday, also for the month of February.
    Small charge for admission.

It has often been said that Darwin's work, "The Origin of Species by Means of Natural Selection", published in 1859, has had more effect on the way people think than any other book ever written. Be that as it may, it certainly revolutionized the natural sciences, and biology in particular, and it is interesting to discover what sort of man brought about this revolution.
    Charles Robert Darwin was born in Shrewsbury (see under Shrewsbury) in 1809. His father was Robert Waring Darwin, a well-to-do country doctor, and his mother's maiden name was Susannah Wedgwood, one of the daughters of Josiah Wedgwood, the founder of the famous pottery and china firm. Charles' mother died when he was only eight, but apart from this he had a happy, though perhaps uninspiring childhood. He was no scholar, and because of this was often at odds with his father. However in 1825, at the age of 16, Charles accompanied his elder brother to Edinburgh University

to study medicine. This only lasted two years, mainly due to his revulsion at operations performed without anaesthetics. He left Edinburgh, and from 1827-1831, he attended Christ's College, Cambridge (see under Cambridge), with the intention of preparing himself for the clergy. However, while at Cambridge, he became a close friend of a brilliant young botany professor, John Stevens Henslow, and it can be said that Henslow altered the course of Darwin's life by instilling in him a deep interest in botany and natural science. Shortly after Darwin left Cambridge, with a poor degree, Professor Henslow recommended him for the post of naturalist on a naval ship about to undertake a long and difficult voyage. Charles was offered and accepted this position, and from 1831-1836, he sailed around the world in H.M.S. Beagle. The voyage of this ship, and its consequences for Darwin, have recently been told in the magnificent seven part B.B.C. production " The Voyage of Charles Darwin". If it is possible to see it, we cannot recommend it too strongly. Certainly anyone who has seen it will want to see Downe. This voyage was the most important event in Charles' life, for it was this that developed him into a mature and critical scientist, and gave rise to all his future theories.

After returning to England (which he never left again) in 1836 he wrote a great deal about his experiences as a naturalist during the voyage, particularly on zoology, botany and geology, and he quickly became known as one of the leading naturalists of his day. In 1839 he married his cousin Emma Wedgwood, and three years later they moved into Down House, where they lived for the rest of their lives. Here on this small estate they raised a family of 10 children (only 7 of whom survived to maturity), and here Darwin, who suffered from chronic ill health, found the peace and solitude he needed to study, to work and to write. It is appropriate to note that the world owes as much to his wife, Emma, as to Darwin himself. For it was she who nursed him for over 40 years and gave him the encouragement, peace and quiet to pursue his work. It is not generally realized that Darwin wrote over 20 books in his lifetime, and over 100 scientific articles. He was a meticulous and thorough worker, to whom time was of little importance in the development of his ideas. in 1837, one year after his return from the voyage of the Beagle, he started a notebook concerning his ideas on "The Transmutation of Species," which later evolved into "The Theory of Evolution by Natural Selection." In 1842 and 1844 he wrote out complete sketches of his theories. These manuscripts survive, but they were never published in his day, he was far too cautious. Finally in 1858, while he was at work on his book concerning evolution, and after receiving the famous letter from Alfred Russel Wallace (see under Broadstone), he and Wallace had a joint paper on the subject read before the Linnean Society of London. It was entitled "On the Tendency of Species to Form Varieties; and On the Perpetuation of Varieties and Species by Means of Selection." The reading, and subsequent publication of this paper, caused little interest, but when in the following year, 1859, "The Origin of Species by Means of Natural Selection" was published the reaction was quite different. The world has in fact never been the same since, for it transformed not only all of biology and became its central theory, but it also transformed man's way of thinking and looking at himself, often described as his place in nature. Darwin quickly became world famous, and although a great deal of abuse was showered upon him, his views were generally welcomed by young scholars but rejected by the old. However they have stood the test of time, and all modern biology is founded on them. Despite his world-wide fame, Darwin's life was not altered. He continued his research and wrote many more books, mostly on botany, which he used to support his central ideas. It is indeed pleasant to record that in 1882 when Darwin died, and despite all the controversy that had surrounded him, so high had his esteem become that he was buried in Westminster Abbey, where the visitor today may see his tombstone.

Down House is preserved much as Darwin left it. The whole of the ground floor is open to the public (the upper floors are privately occupied) and comprises six rooms, the Hall, the New Study, the Drawing Room, the Charles Darwin Room, the Erasmus Darwin Room and the Old Study. The contents of each room are well marked, explained and beautifully displayed. They contain a wealth of information about the life and work of Charles and his family. Most of the furniture is original, including his desk and chair at which he wrote many of his works, including "The Origin." The Old Study is much as he would have known it each day as he went in to work, including its spittoon and sitzbath! Some of his personal library is still there. The ground floor of the house is truly a thrilling place, but after it has been seen, the visitor should not neglect to walk down to the bottom of the garden and around the Sand Walk, where Darwin used to walk almost every day, and which he called his "Thinking Path." Down House is, so to speak, the "Mecca" of biologists, and will not disappoint anyone interested in the history of biology or even the larger realm of human history in general. Our enthusiasm for Down House was also shared by the Darwin family themselves, for in her "Period Piece," Mrs. Gwen Raverat, a grandaughter of Charles Darwin, wrote: "For us, everything at Down was perfect. That was an axiom. And by us I mean, not only the children, but all the uncles and aunts who belonged there - - - everything there was different. And better."

Downe is full of stories about Charles Darwin, and there are other associations which the visitor will hear about, but it is worthwhile mentioning that despite the general hostility of the church and clergy towards Darwin and his theories, there is, on the side of the Church of St. Mary the Virgin, overlooking a sundial and the village square of Downe, the following inscription:

This Sundial is in memory of
Charles Darwin
1809-1882
who lived and worked in Downe
for 40 years
He is buried in Westminster Abbey.

Have lunch at the George and Dragon Pub (where Darwin himself drank his ale) and then walk along Luxted Road to Down House!

EAST KILBRIDE (Lanarkshire), Scotland
Location - About 400 miles north and slightly west of London, and 10 miles east of Glasgow.
Train - From London (Euston) to Glasgow (Central) and then by taxi or bus to East Kilbride.
Road - There are two main routes from London to Glasgow:
    1. Take the M1 north to Leeds, then join the A65 to Skipton and on to entrance 36 of the M6. Go north on the M6 around Carlisle and join the A74 which will join the M74. Take exit 6 which leads along the A74 into Glasgow.
    2. Take the A1 to Scotch Corner and turn left along the A6 to entrance 40 on the M6. Follow the M6 north and join the A74, which will in turn join the M74. Take exit 6 which leads along the A74 into Glasgow.
    To reach East Kilbride from Glasgow by car take the A749 through Rutherglen to East Kilbride. Upon entering the latter take the Calderwood turning, where there is a sign pointing to the Hunter Museum on Maxwellton Road.

Hunter Museum (or Hunter House)
Maxwellton Road
East Kilbride

Phone: East Kilbride 23993 or East Kilbride 41111
Opening hours:
> There are no regular opening hours, but it is only necessary to
> phone in advance for an appointment. There is a Hunter Trust
> which administers the museum under the patronage of the
> Royal College of Surgeons and the University of Glasgow.
> Small charge for admission.

Seldom have two such brilliant men come from the same family
as William (1718-1783) and John (1728-1793) Hunter, both of
whom distinguished themselves as doctors, and left lasting
contributions to medicine. Both were born in the little house, now
referred to as Hunter House. For an account of John Hunter, see
under The Royal College of Surgeons, London, but a brief account
of William will be given here.

As a boy William Hunter attended grammar school in East
Kilbride, and at 13 he entered the University of Glasgow where he
studied the humanities and the classics. After four years at the
university he was apprenticed as a medical student to a Dr. William
Cullen in Hamilton. It is important to realize that in the 18th century
there were still no medical schools as we know them today, and a
student of medicine simply picked up as best he could the
knowledge of the day, which was not only very little but often wrong
as well. Dr. Cullen had a great influence on William, and as a result of
this he went on to study medicine at the University of Edinburgh, as
well as in London and Paris. He was very impressed with the manner
in which anatomy was taught in Paris, by dissection, and on
returning to London in 1746 he set up his own anatomy school
which was, for its day, of such high quality and so successful that it
lasted until his death in 1783. As part of his school he set up one of
the first anatomy museums in the world so that students could study
the specimens, both normal and pathological on a year-round basis.
In London, William went from medical honor to medical honor, and
finally became obstetrician to the Queen, whom he attended during
her first pregnancy in 1762, and it was in obstetrics that he made his
greatest and lasting contributions. Prior to this time obstetrics was
based on a vast array of ignorance and superstition and was in the

hands of quacks and untrained midwives. Hunter led the way in putting it on a scientific basis.

In 1774, after 25 years of study and collecting scientific information, he published his classic work "The Anatomy of the Human Gravid Uterus." It was by far the best book on the pregnant uterus ever published, and with it obstetrics as a science was ushered in. It contained 34 magnificent engravings of the pregnant uterus by the artist Jan van Rymsdyck, and was dedicated to the King (George III). The original copy of this with text in both Latin and English, together with the hand-done illustrations of the artist are housed in the Special Collections Department of the main library of the University of Glasgow on University Avenue. It may be seen by permission of the librarian, and it is worth the effort!

During his lifetime, and in addition to his museum specimens, William amassed valuable and extensive collections of books, pictures and coins, all of which he left to the University of Glasgow, where they can be seen today (see under Glasgow), and are very impressive. He died in London in 1783, but medicine, and obstetrics in particular, owes an eternal debt of gratitude to William Hunter.

On the outside of the Hunter House is a plaque which reads as follows:

The Birthplace of Two Great Scotsmen
William Hunter and John Hunter
Born 23 May 1718   Born 13 Feb 1728
Died 30 March 1783   Died 16 Oct 1793
Pre-eminent in Medicine and in Surgery.

The house, including the barn and garden, is much as it was in the Hunters' day and has been nicely preserved, despite a modern development all around it. On the ground floor is a one room museum, with a wealth of interesting Hunterian material as well as various items of medical interest from the 18th century. The visitor can also see by request the tiny first floor room where both William and John Hunter were born. Hunter House is in a somewhat out of the way place, but the effort of going to see the birthplace of these two great Scotsmen is well worth it.

EAST WELLOW (Hampshire)
Location - 85 miles southwest of London, near Romsey.
Train - London (Waterloo) to Romsey, and then by taxi.

Road - Take the M3 or A30 from London to beyond Basingstoke
        and join the A33 around Winchester. Then fork right along
        the A32 to Romsey. At Romsey take the A27 towards
        Salisbury, but after about 2 miles turn left to "The Wellows"
        and follow signs to East Wellow.

Church of St. Margaret of Antioch
East Wellow
Hampshire

It is in this churchyard that Florence Nightingale (see under St.
Thomas' Hospital, London) is buried. One might have imagined that
so great a benefactor of mankind as Florence Nightingale, would
have been buried in Westminster Abbey, but during her long life
she always spurned publicity and honors, and was no different in
death. She is buried in a common grave alongside other members
of her family. The grave is easily found, being only a few yards from
the main entrance to the church, and has a prominent spire above
the tombstone with inscriptions on it of the family buried there.
Florence Nightingale is inscribed simply as F.N. with her birth and
death dates. Inside the church is a plaque dedicated to her, and on
the porch is one of her famous lamps, which her family gave to the
church.

The reason Florence Nightingale is buried at East Wellow, is
that nearby her family owned a large house, Embley Park. It is now a
school (Embley Park School), but the outside of the main building is
much the same as in the 19th century, and still in the beautiful
setting that Florence Nightingale knew. It is located on the south
side of the A27, between The Wellows sign and where the road
joins A31 near Romsey. The house is clearly marked at the main
gate. There is no harm in driving in to see the exterior and its
setting, but the building itself is private.

EDINBURGH (Lothian), Scotland
Location - 375 miles north of London.
Train - From London (King's Cross) to Edinburgh (Waverly). From
        Glasgow (Queens) to Edinburgh (Waverly).
Road - Take the M1 or A1 to Scotch Corner, and then fork right to
        Durham and Newcastle. At Newcastle join the A696 to
        Ponteland, and at Otterburn this joins the A68 to Dalkeith
        and Edinburgh.

Edinburgh is one of the most ancient and beautiful cities in Britain, which in addition to many cultural and political aspects, has a famous scientific history centered in its great university. During the 18th and 19th centuries it had one of the most distinguished medical schools in the world.

Sir James Young Simpson Museum
52 Queen Street
Edinburgh

Opening hours:
Normal business hours. The museum is maintained by the Royal College of Surgeons of Edinburgh, but the house is used as a shelter by the Church of Scotland.
No charge for admission.

Sir James Young Simpson has a permanent place in the history of medicine, not only for his great contributions to obstetrics, but above all for his discovery in 1847 of the anaesthetic properties of chloroform. This became the worldwide standard anaesthetic for nearly 100 years, and has only been generally superseded in very recent times.

Simpson was born at Bathgate, the son of a baker, David Simpson. It is said that his mother, who died tragically when he was only nine, decided very early on that young James should be the scholar of the family. He did not disappoint her! While in his early teens, he attended arts classes in Edinburgh, but very soon switched to medicine, and at the early age of 19 became a member of the Royal College of Surgeons. Soon after he was practicing medicine in Edinburgh, with a specialty of obstetrics at which he spent most of his life. It is of great interest that Charles Darwin and James Young Simpson were both medical students at Edinburgh at the same time. However, it is of even greater interest that they were both revolted by operations performed without anaesthetics. Because of this Darwin gave up medicine and went on to other things, but fortunately Simpson decided to try to do something about it. It is worthwhile recording in this respect the actual operation which had such an influence on Simpson, because it will help the modern reader to understand how surgery has changed over the past 150 years. This operation was an amputation of the breast of a woman, and was performed by Robert Liston, one of the most famous surgeons of his day. The normal procedure for this was simply to lift up the soft tissue of the breast with an instrument resembling a hook, thus enabling the surgeon to sweep around the mass with his knife, hopefully in two clean cuts! Simpson, like other medical students (all males in those days), had seen other operations and was keen to see this one. However, as Liston picked up his knife, Simpson observed the horrified look of terror on the woman's face and turned away leaving the room. In those days one of the major attributes of a surgeon was the speed with which he could perform the operation. Operations had to be performed in a matter of seconds, rather than minutes, otherwise the patient would almost certainly die of shock. Liston was a master of the art, of whom Simpson himself remarked that "he amputated with such speed that the sound of sawing seemed to succeed immediately the first flash of the knife." From that moment onwards Simpson determined to try to do something to relieve the pain suffered in operations and since he specialized in obstetrics, he also quickly became concerned to try to relieve the pain suffered by women in childbirth. Doctors at that time had to be somewhat indifferent to the pain suffered by their patients for they could do nothing about it, but Simpson set himself the task of trying to reverse this, and was indeed successful beyond his wildest hopes.

In the first half of the 19th century, mesmerism was popular as a pain reliever. Simpson tried this in 1837, and also other methods as they became available but all were very unsatisfactory. In 1845 there were no safe or reliable methods of testing new drugs, but Simpson and his two assistants, Dr. George Keith and Dr. Matthew Duncan, undertook to test a whole variety of available drugs on themselves. Their method was simple almost to the point of absurdity! After dinner at night, Simpson and his two assistants sat around the dining table, poured out a sample of a drug into a saucer, and proceeded to smell it and describe its effects. They had some horrible experiences, needless to say, and on more than one occasion Simpson nearly died from the effects of the drugs. However they pressed on in their quest, and after dinner on the 4th of November 1847, they all inhaled a sample of chloroform. Very rapidly they became unconscious and slipped under the table. Upon recovery Simpson knew at once that he had discovered something important and hoped it would be the answer to his search. Within a week he lectured on it at the university, within two weeks it was used in an operation at the Royal Infirmary, and within a month Simpson had used it on his female patients in childbirth. It must be pointed out that this was not really the first operation at which an anaesthetic was used. The credit for this is usually given to the two American dentists Morton and Wells (see under Boston and

Washington, U.S.A.) who used ether and nitrous oxide. As a result of their discovery (just prior to the discovery of chloroform) Simpson also tried ether in childbirth, but it proved dangerous and very unsatisfactory, while chloroform was quite the reverse, and proved to be very reliable.

One might have thought that Simpson would immediately have been hailed as a great human benefactor, but that was not the case. Many surgeons opposed the use of chloroform in operations, because they thought that the pain suffered during these was good for the patient's character and "moral fibre"! However, it was for its use in childbirth that the worst abuse was hurled at Simpson. Was he not flying in the face of Providence?-- for did not the Bible decree "-- in sorrow thou shalt bring forth children; --" (Genesis 3:16). Needless to say, there were those (mostly men) who believed passionately that the pains of childbirth were also good for the woman's character! Fortunately, Simpson himself was a devout Christian, and he patiently but firmly answered abuse by the critics, and the opposition gradually faded. The final "seal of approval" was given in 1853 when no less a person than Queen Victoria (the titular head of the Church of England) accepted chloroform at the birth of her eighth child. In so doing she did all women a great service. The use of chloroform quickly spread around the world, a new era of surgery was ushered in, because speed was no longer a criterion, and women were relieved of the worst pangs of childbirth. But more than this, Simpson's discovery and humanitarian attitude as an obstetrician, raised the status of women above that of some kind of "second class" human being. Unfortunately, Simpson's fight is still not completely won.

For his services to humanity James Young Simpson was knighted by Queen Victoria in 1866 and when he died in 1870, the city of Edinburgh gave him a funeral the likes of which the city had never seen before nor since. It was hoped by many that he would be buried in Westminster Abbey, but his widow, remaining true to the nature of her husband as a simple man, declined the offer.

At 52 Queen Street in Edinburgh stands the house where Simpson lived for the last 25 years of his life, and where also he died in 1870. In his day it was much more than a family residence. Here he and his assistants dealt with a constant stream of patients, and bedrooms were provided for those who came from a distance. There was also a constant influx of visitors, including medical men seeking advice. The outside of the house is marked with a plaque which reads as follows:

Sir James Young Simpson
lived in this house from 1845 to 1870
and in 1847 discovered
the anaesthetic power of
CHLOROFORM.

Most of the inside of the house is generally unaltered, but is now used for the purposes of the Church of Scotland. However on the ground floor is Simpson's dining room, in which the anaesthetic properties of chloroform were discovered. It survives intact and is known as "The Discovery Room." You can ask permission of the person on duty for the Church of Scotland to see the room, and they will also give you a pamphlet on the life of Simpson. To us this room is an absolute gem in human and medical history, and still remains much as Simpson and his family would have known it. His huge dining table is still there, together with the cabinets and other furniture that he used while testing the drugs. On the mantlepiece are his wood foetal stethoscopes, his crucifix which he used as a knife, his pill box, Lady Simpson's bible, and his brandy decanter, into which he poured the chloroform on the evening of November 4, 1847. This can only be described as "true dedication"! In addition to this memorial to Simpson, the city of Edinburgh has erected a fine statue of him. It is considerably larger than life, and is located on the south side of Princes Street near the corner of South Charlotte Street. He is always depicted smiling, and this surely has some meaning!

University of Edinburgh
Old College
South Bridge
Edinburgh

Opening hours:
Normal business hours.
No charge for admission.

The origins of the University of Edinburgh go back beyond 1583, but in that year the first students in Arts and Divinity were formally enrolled and from that time onwards it has had a distinguished history, particularly in medicine in the 19th century.

Joseph Lister (see under Glasgow) was in Edinburgh both before and after his stay in Glasgow (1860-1869), which was where he did his monumental work on antiseptic therapy. He was in Edinburgh from 1854-1860 as a young assistant to a famous surgeon of his day, James Syme, and returned to Edinburgh again in 1869 as Regius Professor of Clinical Surgery at the university, remaining there until 1877. The house in which he lived during this time is at 9 Charlotte Square (north side) and is marked by a plaque, but it is privately owned. Lister always felt it was the University of Edinburgh that gave him his start in a distinguished medical career, and in gratitude he left all his many honors to the University at Edinburgh. These are located within the Quad of the Old College and are displayed in a large case at the head of the main staircase leading to a beautiful Library Hall. They can be seen with the permission of the Bedellus of the university. It is a truly remarkable display, and gives some indication of the esteem in which Lister was held in his day, as well as what we of later generations owe to him. Above the case is a portrait of Lister by J.H. Lorimer. The Library Hall (built 1827) should also be seen, with its array of busts of all the famous professors of the university, as well as such interesting things as the library table of Sir Walter Scott, and Napoleon's table from his study on the Island of St. Helena. There are a host of other historical associations of the University of Edinburgh, and it was here that Charles Darwin (see under Downe) and his elder brother Erasmus attended medical school. In fact they both lived just around the corner from the Old College at 11 Lothian Street. Their house is now unfortunately completely gone, a victim of redeve - lopment.

The Royal Infirmary of Edinburgh
Lauriston Place
Edinburgh

Opening hours:
>Normal business hours.
>No charge for admission.

This is the modern Royal Infirmary of Edinburgh, which is a huge complex of hospitals, dating from 1870. In addition to his professorship at the university, Lister had an appointment here during his second stay in Edinburgh, and he lectured in the so-called Lister Theatre. Also as part of the Royal Infirmary is a James

Young Simpson Maternity Wing, and inside the main rotunda is a large and striking portrait of Simpson by Norman Macbeth.

The Old Royal Infirmary of Edinburgh and Surgeons Hall
12 High School Wynd (corner of Infirmary Street)
Edinburgh

Opening hours:
> Normal business hours.
> No charge for admission.

These two buildings were originally a high school, then became the surgical hospital of the Royal Infirmary, and are now the Geography Department of the university. Both Lister and Syme worked here in the surgical wards and extended the use of antiseptic therapy which Lister had developed earlier in Glasgow. The interiors of these buildings have been much altered since Lister's day but the exteriors are almost the same. It is a tragedy that the fine old lecture theater that Lister used has been altered almost beyond recognition. The fact that Lister and Syme both worked here is commemorated by a nice plaque at the front entrance which reads as follows:

> James Syme (1833-1869)
> and
> Joseph Lister (1869-1877)
>
> While Regius Professors of Clinical
> Surgery in the Universtiy of Edinburgh
> had charge of the wards in this building
> then the Old Surgical Hospital
> and part of
> The Royal Infirmary of Edinburgh
>
> Erected by Surgeons of Toronto-Canada 1957.

The Royal College of Surgeons of Edinburgh
Nicholson Street
Edinburgh

Opening hours:
> Normal business hours.
> No charge for admission.

The Royal College of Surgeons of Edinburgh is the Scottish counterpart of the Royal College of Surgeons of England, and is primarily responsible for the maintenance and improvement of the standards of surgery in Scotland. In this regard the college has played a long and distiguished role in surgical history. Both Lister and Syme, as well as Simpson, were Fellows of the college. Like most of these colleges, it is large and imposing both outside and in, and has a fine collection of portraits of its distinguished Fellows. There is a very valuable and extensive medical library going back five centuries. The library also has a small number of Lister's letters, notes, testimonials etc., but a much larger collection of materials relating to the work of Simpson, which includes many letters and other correspondence refering to anaesthesia as well as his lecture notes. The library is not open to the public, but permission to see it may be requested. One may also ask to see the very interesting museum on the top floor of the building. This is mostly pathology, but there are also some very interesting historical rooms as well. In these rooms are a Lister case with various items which belonged to him, including some of his carbolic acid machines for making carbolic bandages, carbolic acid sprays, various instruments and photographs of his surgical wards. There is also a Simpson case with many items of great interest, and a Benjamin Bell (1749-1806) case. Dr. Benjamin Bell is rightly famous for enormously advancing our knowledge of venereal disease. There are other displays, including one on Robert Liston (1794-1847), who was referred to earlier, and was known popularly as "the fastest man with a knife!" All in all the Royal College of Surgeons of Edinburgh is a very interesting place.

The Royal Society of Edinburgh
22 George Street
Edinburgh

Opening hours:
> Normal business hours.
> No charge for admission.

This is the "younger brother" of the Royal Society of London. Founded in 1783, it has done a great deal to maintain and lift the quality of scientific development in Scotland. The building in which it is currently housed, is very imposing inside with beautiful architecture, and portraits of famous Scots who have been Fellows of the society. The library, which is of the utmost importance in its historical holdings, is unfortunately hopelessly overcrowded. Nevertheless it is a marvelous sight to see, and the secretary is happy to give you a short tour of the premises.

The Royal College of Physicians of Edinburgh
9 Queen Street
Edinburgh

Opening hours:
> Normal business hours.
> No charge for admission.

The founding of this organization goes back to 1681, and since then its functions have not changed. They are to promote and advance the quality of medicine in Scotland. In this capacity they maintain and improve standards, promote research, organize meetings, etc., and maintain one of the best medical libraries in the world. As well as their modern working library, they have a total of 200,000 volumes going back hundreds of years, and hold virtually every important work in the history of medicine. The college is closely associated with Sir James Young Simpson, who was its President from 1850-1852, and the library holds most of Simpson's own library, his casebooks, lecture notes, letters, etc., a priceless collection. Throughout the building there are huge portraits of famous Scottish physicians, including one of Simpson by Norman Macbeth. The college is not normally open to the public, but interested visitors can ask to be shown over it, and we found those in charge very cooperative.

The Royal Botanic Garden of Edinburgh
Arboretum Road
Edinburgh

Opening hours:
> Monday-Saturday, 9.00-sunset.
> Sunday, 11.00-sunset.
> Small charge for admission.
> The main entrance is the west gate on Arboretum Road. The library and herbarium are on Inverleith Row near the east gate.

The Royal Botanic Garden of Edinburgh is second only to Kew (see Kew) in Britain, and is one of the great botanic gardens of the world. It is a National Garden funded mainly by the Scottish Office of the British Government, and its primary function is research in the taxonomy of plants. Like so many other botanic gardens it started out as a physic garden in 1670, but has steadily evolved to play a large role in the development of scientific botany. It also fills great educational and informational needs. In addition to the gardens themselves with their numerous array of plants, there is a modern herbarium with nearly two million plant specimens from all over the world, and one of the best botanical libraries in existence. The library holdings go back to a 1486 herbal, and there are over 3000 pre-Linnean manuscripts and books. Many of the works of Linnaeus are in their original editions and there is also an extensive collection of the great floras of the 18th and 19th centuries. The library may be viewed by the public, but can only be used by permission of the librarian.

FOLKESTONE (Kent)

Location - 63 miles southeast of London.
Train - From London (Victoria).
Road - Take the A20 in south London and follow this, or the M20,
     to Maidstone, Ashford and on to Folkestone.

Folkestone is a seaport on the southeast coast of England, and is one of the traditional gateways to the continent. As such it has a long and interesting history, but to us none of it is more interesting than the fact that this was the birthplace of William Harvey (1578-1657). (See also under Ashford, Hempstead and Padua, Italy).

At the end of the 16th century, peoples' knowledge of animal physiology was not only primitive, but full of misconceptions. It was known that blood probably had a nutritional function, but our modern concept of blood as a tissue with many vital functions such as nutritional, respiratory, waste disposal, transport of hormones, etc., was not understood. The ideas concerning blood and its functions were derived primarily from the Greek philosopher, Aristotle (384-322 B.C.), and the Greco-Roman physician, Galen (d.200 A.D.), who besides being a very able observer and theorist, was also personal physician to the Roman Emperor Marcus Aurelius (121-180). Unfortunately it takes a good deal of anatomical knowledge to understand how Aristotle and Galen thought of the way in which blood functions, and it is not appropriate to attempt that here. Suffice it to say that neither of them had any concept of blood circulation, and without this, an understanding of its functions is impossible. Galen's view that blood flowed in a back and forth motion, like the ebb and flow of a tide, generally prevailed, and for nearly fourteen centuries his theories went almost unquestioned. It was the young Englishman, William Harvey, who was not only to question them, but to make the revolutionary discovery of blood circulation, and thus lead the way to our present understanding of all the varied functions of this vital tissue. As a result of his discovery Harvey is often described as "the father of modern medicine." Be that as it may, he is certainly the last of the "old" and a giant of the "new."

William Harvey came from yeoman farmer stock, and was the oldest of seven sons. His father was a prominent citizen of Folkestone and became mayor several times. In due course, young William attended King's School, Canterbury and later Gonville and Caius College, Cambridge, where he studied arts and medicine. Upon graduating from Cambridge, Harvey attended the University of Padua, Italy (see under Padua), where he received a doctorate in medicine in 1602. One may ask, why did Harvey go to Padua? The reason is simple. At that time the University of Padua was the leading center of medicine in the world. Amongst Harvey's many famous teachers there was Girolamo Fabricius (1537-1619), who in 1574 discovered the valves in the veins, which permit blood to flow in only one direction. With such discoveries as this at hand, and the stimulating atmosphere of research and inquiry, there can be no doubt that the University of Padua had a profound effect on the development of Harvey's thought.

Upon returning to England, Harvey set up in medical practice in London. In 1604 he married Elizabeth Browne, but the marriage although happy, never produced any children. In 1607 Harvey was elected a Fellow of the Royal College of Physicians, where he frequently lectured to students, and was closely associated with the college for the rest of his life. In 1609 he was also appointed physician to St. Bartholomew's Hospital, but even more important, in 1618 he became a physician to King James I, a position which was carried on with the accession of Charles I in 1625, and whom he followed throughout the Civil War. Unfortunately Harvey never had a permanent home of his own. Most of his life he lived at a house in Whitehall, but in 1642 it was vandalized and many of his notes, manuscripts, etc. were lost. An even worse distaster overtook his personal library, as this and all his other papers and lecture notes were burnt when the Royal College of Physicians perished in the Great Fire of London in 1666. Thus we are left with very few original documents emanating from the pen of William Harvey. What a tragedy!

As early as 1616, Harvey was conducting original investigations into the motions of the heart, and many other aspects of animal physiology. It was the former that attracted his attention most, and in 1628 his masterwork was published in Frankfurt, Germany. This was written in Latin and entitled "Exercitatio Anatomica de Motu Cordis et Sanguinis in Animalibus" (Anatomical Disquisition on the Motion of the Heart and Blood in Animals). Medicine and biology have never been the same since! In this work, not only did Harvey clearly put forth the theory that blood circulated within the body of animals, but as a result of careful observation and experimentation he demonstrated this to be a fact beyond reasonable doubt. However new ideas seldom have a smooth passage, and a contemporary of Harvey's, John Aubrey, describes from Harvey's own words the fate of his great discovery, "I have heard him say, that after the Booke of the Circulation of Blood came out, that he fell mightily in his Practize, and that 'twas believed by the vulgar that he was crack-brained; and all the Physitians were against his Opinion, and enveyed him; many wrote against him. With much adoe at last, in about 20 or 30 years time, it was received in all the Universities in the world." Harvey was a giant of medicine, a master observer, theorist and experimenter, and it is on his work and methods that modern medicine rests today. Harvey died in 1657 at his brother Eliab's house in Roehampton (now a suburb of London), and is buried at Hempstead, Essex (see under Hempstead).

Anyone going to Folkestone to see Harveyian history should try to contact Mr. Walter Montcrieff, who runs an excellent men's tailors and outfitters store in Sandgate (town center). Mr. Montcrieff, a former mayor of Folkestone, and later an alderman, is very knowledgeable about matters "Harveyian" in general. He has done an enormous amount to foster Folkestone's relationship with Harvey. Mr. Montcrieff is very enthusiastic, cooperative and full of information. It is known exactly where Harvey was born in Folkestone, but the house no longer stands. However there is a plaque there commemorating the event. It is on the side of a building on Church Street, near the corner of Rendezvous Road, and reads as follows:

> Near this spot was born on 1st April 1578
> WILLIAM HARVEY
> The world renowned scientist and
> discoverer of the circulation of the blood.
> His father and mother
> attended the nearby parish church
> and his father was mayor of Folkestone
> in the years 1586, 1599, 1601 and 1611.

In the nearby parish church, there is also a plaque in remembrance of the family. Folkestone has also honored her famous son by erecting a very fine statue of him. It was sculptured by A. B. Joy in 1881 and erected the same year. The statue stands in The Leas (the very lovely promenade) near the bandstand, with Harvey looking out across the sea towards the continent. It is beautifully preserved and cared for, and every year on Harvey's birthday there is a "flower laying" ceremony commemorating this event.

GLASGOW (Lanarkshire), Scotland

Location - 400 miles north and slightly west of London.

Train - From London (Euston) to Glasgow (Central). From Edinburgh (Waverly) to Glasgow (Queens).

Road - There are two main routes from London:

    1. Take the M1 north to Leeds, then join the A65 to Skipton and join the M6 at entrance 36. Continue on the M6 around Carlisle and join the A74 which will in turn join the M74. Take exit 6 to Glasgow along the A74.

    2. Take the A1 to Scotch Corner, and fork left along the A66 to entrance 40 on the M6. Continue on the M6 and join the A74, which in turn joins the M74. Take exit 6 along the A74 to Glasgow.

Glasgow is by far the largest city in Scotland. Lying astride the river Clyde on the west coast, its history is lost in time, but the name is derived form a Celtic word meaning "dear green spot," and this well expresses the feelings that its modern citizens have for their city. Like Edinburgh, Glasgow has many places of great interest in the history of biology and medicine.

The Glasgow Royal Infirmary
82-84 Castle Street
Glasgow

Opening hours:
Normal business hours.
No charge for admission.

It was here in the Royal Infirmary between 1861 and 1869 that Joseph Lister (1827-1912) - see also under Edinburgh and London- worked out the basic techniques of antiseptic surgery and first applied them. It is virtually impossible to exaggerate the importance of this event in the history of biology, medicine and human welfare.

Joseph Lister was born in 1827 at Upton, Essex, the second son of Joseph Jackson Lister, a brilliant designer of microscopes, to whom we owe the modern perfection of the objective lens system, which led to the production of the achromatic microscope. Both his father and his mother, Isabella, supplied young Joseph with a happy and intellectually stimulating home, in which, from the very earliest age, he was encouraged to observe, explore and investigate for himself. He attended local schools, where he was a good student, and in 1844 at the age of 17 entered University College, London, receiving a BA degree in 1847. He immediately entered medical school, but his studies were considerably delayed because he contracted smallpox, and did not receive his medical degree until 1852. At the same time he became a Fellow of the Royal College of Surgeons. The following year, however, he was appointed an assistant to James Syme, the famous professor of clinical surgery at Edinburgh. Here Lister established himself as a brilliant and original investigator, an able surgeon and an excellent teacher. He also married Agnes Syme, "the boss' daughter" (a good thing to do then as now!), who was his devoted wife for nearly 40 years. Anaesthesia, introduced some years before, was now used regularly at operations, and it is interesting to note that Lister, while a student, may have been present in 1846 at University College Hospital, London, when the first operation in England using ether was performed by Robert Liston (see under Edinburgh). The introduction of anaesthesia for operations was undoubtedly the greatest advance in surgery in all its history, but there remained one overriding problem. Before operations could be considered reasonably safe, there was the problem of infection, the overall death rate from which ran as high as 40%. Lister, a very sensitive man, was appalled at this, and determined to do something about it. His extraordinary abilities were recognized when he was elected a Fellow of the Royal Society in 1860, and the same year was appointed Regius Professor of Surgery at the University of Glasgow, and a year later was appointed to the Glasgow Royal Infirmary. It was here at the Royal Infirmary that his inventive mind was put to work on what we now know as antiseptic surgery. As early as 1861 and again in 1864 Louis Pasteur (see under Paris, Arbois and Dôle, France) had published some remarkable work which gave the clue to the possible "germ theory" of infection. Lister quickly became aware of this, and realized that germs might be the cause of operative infections. In 1865 he performed the first successful treatment using a carbolic acid dressing as an antiseptic agent. As his techniques improved the results were almost miraculous, and the death rate from infection dropped dramatically. Lister described his results in a series of papers, the first of which was published in Lancet in 1867. It was entitled "On a new Method of treating Compound Fracture, Abscess etc. With Observations on the Conditions of Suppuration" (suppuration means the formation of pus or festering). It is one of the great works of medicine, and paved the way for a whole new era in surgery and antiseptic therapy of all kinds. Lister's ideas invoked much opposition and skepticism, and his techniques spread only slowly around the world, being gradually improved upon. In 1869 Lister returned to the University of Edinburgh for eight years, then to King's College, London, until 1893. In that year his wife, Agnes, died, a blow from which he really never recovered. Nevertheless, he carried on with his major responsibilities, and honors continued to be showered upon him, including a peerage from Queen Victoria in 1897. He was the first surgeon to ever receive such an honor. He died in 1912 at Walmer, Kent, and although it was universally hoped he would be buried in Westminster Abbey, he himself declined the honor preferring to be buried beside his wife in Hampstead Cemetery (see under London).

Most of the present buildings of the Royal Infirmary date from about 1905-1915 (there has been constant new construction), and despite great efforts on the part of many people nothing survives of the wards where Lister actually did his work. However, his great achievements, not only in antiseptic treatment, but also in early and successful attempts in plastic surgery, are commemorated by two plaques. The first is on the outside wall of the infirmary, and can be seen from Castle Street. It reads as follows:

On this site stood the Surgical
Wards in which from 1861-1869
Joseph Lister
Surgeon to the Royal Infirmary
and Regius Professor of Surgery
in the University of Glasgow
initiated the method of antiseptic treatment.

The second plaque, along with various busts, is inside the
lobby of the main entrance, and reads:

LISTER
From 1861-1869, Surgeon to this
Infirmary where he originated
the antiseptic system of surgical treatment.
Presented to the Infirmary by the past and
present members of the staff
1908.

Some idea of the dramatic success of Lister's antiseptic
surgical treatment is important. When he initiated it in 1865
casualties from operations dropped almost overnight by about two
thirds. Yet there were many who for a long time not only doubted
the validity of his methods, but positively despised him and
considered him a quack.

When Lister died, much of his library was dispersed and sold
at auction, but thanks to Professor John Hammond Teacher, some
of it was bought in 1913 from the London book dealer Henry
Sotheran for the then "horrendous" sum of £29.16.0! and these
books are now in a small museum located in the Pathology
Department. Actually the major part of this museum comprises the
pathological specimens of William Hunter (see under East Kilbride),
but there are two cases of Lister relics and more may be added when
the current renovation of the museum is completed. In addition to
Lister's books and manuscripts, there are some of his very
interesting and early carbolic acid sprays, a set of his bougies,
fermentation tubes and various other instruments. Also preserved
is his operating stool and a model of his operating table. The
Pathology Department Museum is not open to the public on a
regular basis, but permission to see it may usually be obtained by
interested visitors.

The Royal College of Physicians and Surgeons of Glasgow

234-242 St. Vincent Street
Glasgow

Opening hours:
Normal business hours.
No charge for admission.

The Royal College of Physicians and Surgeons of Glasgow was founded by Maister Peter Lowe in 1599 under a charter granted by James VI of Scotland. Peter Lowe had spent most of his life up until the age of 50 in the service of the King of France, and was a contemporary of Ambroise Paré (1509-1590) whom he probably knew. It seems likely that he trained in the school at Orleans, and he certainly became a member of the Faculté de Chirurgerie in Paris. In any case he set the Royal College of Physicians and Surgeons of Glasgow on a sound footing, which it has maintained ever since, and the college has done an enormous amount over the centuries to advance the cause of medicine. Since the college has had such a long and continuous history, its library contains a copy of virtually every major work published in the field of medicine, and with 300,000 volumes it is one of the great medical libraries of the world. It is interesting that in addition to its priceless medical collections, the library also contains such items as a first edition of Audubon's "Birds of America." For the interest of collectors, a copy of this work was recently sold at Sotheby's in London for over one million dollars!

Joseph Lister was a Fellow of the college, and within the college is a case containing very interesting medical instruments belonging originally to him. They include carbolic acid sprays, a cupping set and microscopes. There is also a so-called "Lister Room" which contains the fireplace from the Lister Ward in the Royal Infirmary -- a reminder of the main means of heating in those days! The library collections include many books and manuscripts of Lister's, also many of his lecture notes, and even notes taken by his students at his lectures (very valuable to professional historians). They also possess the complete correspondence between Lister and Sir William McEwen (who worked under Lister). This correspondence is very important, because in it is recorded their early ideas concerning the development of antiseptic surgery.

It is a pleasure to record that the premises of the college are beautifully maintained, and that it continues the tradition of its long history. The college itself can only be used by the Fellows, but interested visitors may ask the Head Librarian to be shown over the building and their priceless collections. We found the staff enthusiastic and cooperative.

The University of Glasgow
University Avenue
Glasgow

Opening hours:
>Normal business hours.
>No charge for admission.

The University of Glasgow dates back to 1451. It is one of the main universities of Britain, and has always played a major role in the development of Glasgow and Scotland. Many brilliant people, particularly in science, have studied or developed their ideas there, and their names are recorded on the beautiful front gates of the university. Incidentally, just within the front gates is the Hunter Memorial commemorating the two great Scotsmen William and John Hunter (see also under East Kilbride and London). For our purposes, however, there are two important people closely associated with the University of Glasgow. These are Joseph Lister (see also under Edinburgh and London) and William Hunter.

Lister was Regius Professor of Surgery at the university from 1860-1869, and his important work during these years has been described (above) under the Royal Infirmary. It is remarkable, however, that this great man has left so little trace at the university he served with such distinction. They did have some of his instruments, manuscripts and notes, but even these have been transferred to the Science Museum in London, for incorporation in the "Lister Room" of the new medical science wing (see under London).

Fortunately, it is quite a different story with William Hunter. He attended Glasgow University as a student, but never taught there. However, he always felt that he owed a lot to the university, and when he died he bequeathed to it his huge collections of books and manuscripts, anatomical, pathological and zoological dissections, as well as other items such as minerals and coins. Some of these are housed in the Hunterian Museum. His art collection is in the Art Gallery. His pathological dissections are in the Royal Infirmary, referred to earlier, but his zoological dissections are in the museum of the Zoology Department of the university, and may be seen upon request at the Zoology Department office. His anatomical

46

dissections are in the Anatomy Museum of the Department of Anatomy, and may be seen upon request at the Anatomy Department office. These anatomy dissections are superb, and are housed in a beautifully well-kept "period piece" museum.

Finally, William Hunter's books and manuscripts are housed in the Special Collections Department of the Main Library, which is just off University Avenue. These may be seen by permission of the librarian in charge. Perhaps their most valued item is not only an original edition of Hunter's "The Anatomy of the Gravid Uterus" (referred to earlier), but also a description of the time of year the specimens were obtained which was vital to their preservation! The Special Collections Department contains many other priceless medical and biological books, which is consistent with the university's long and distinguished history.

Glasgow Botanic Gardens
Queen Margaret Drive and Great Western Road
Glasgow

Opening hours:
> Gardens, 7.00- dusk.
> Glasshouses, 13.00-16.30.
> No charge for admission.

The Glasgow Botanic Gardens started in 1801 as a Physic Garden attached to the Medical School of the university. In 1818 it obtained a Royal Charter and the gardens became the Royal Botanical Institute. In 1820 Sir William Hooker (see under Kew) became its director. For the next 20 years under Hooker's direction the garden prospered, and became one of the great botanic gardens of the world. Then as now, Glasgow was a flourishing sea port, and plants from all over the world poured into the Royal Botanical Institute. In 1840 Hooker went to London as director of Kew Gardens, and at the same time the gardens were moved to their present location in Kelvinside. It is a pity that in due course the Royal Botanical Institute lost its Royal Charter and came under the control of the City of Glasgow. This inevitably meant that its research and scientific botanical functions declined, and it now has mainly educational functions, specializing in orchids, begonias, economic plants and the breeding of plants. They also have a marvelous historical botanic library. Perhaps their past is greater than their present, but the gardens are still well worth a visit.

Glasgow is a city not normally on the main tourist route, but it is of great interest for biological and medical history. There are also a host of other cultural aspects. If we may make a suggestion, don't miss a pleasure trip down the river Clyde to "The Isles"!

GOSPORT (Hampshire)

Location - 70 miles southwest of London, on the west side of Portsmouth Harbour.

Train - From London (Waterloo) to Portsmouth and then by taxi or ferry to Gosport.

Road - Take the A3 from London through Guildford and at Petersfield turn right onto the A272 and follow this to where it joins the A32. On the A32 take the left turn to Wickham, Fareham and Gosport.

Gosport is a naval town, and was a major embarkation point for hundreds of thousands of allied soldiers on and after D-day in 1944, and has been a Royal Navy base for hundreds of years.

The Medical Museum
Royal Naval Hospital
Haslar
Gosport

Phone - Gosport 070-17-84255
Opening hours:
    By phoning in advance to the Commanding Officer.
    Children are not admitted.
    No charge for admission.

The Royal Naval Hospital, Haslar, is on a spit of land at the southeast tip of Gosport, and as part of the hospital there is a very good medical museum. The hospital and museum were bombed in 1941 and there was much damage. However, everything has been repaired and restored and the medical museum is very interesting. It has three aspects which cannot easily be separated:

1. The purely historical medical aspect.
2. The natural history aspect, which derives from the great Royal Navy voyages of discovery in the 18th and 19th centuries.
3. The superb historical library of about 6,000 volumes.

Some of the priceless books include:
1. "Birds of Australia," 7 volumes, John Gould.
2. "Of the cure of the scurvey," James Lind. 1st edition, 1753, 2nd edition 1757. In which he performed one of the first "controlled experiments."
3. "A Voyage to Jamaica," Hans Sloane, 1707.
4. "History of the World," Sir Walter Raleigh, 1677. This also contains a history of his life and trial.

There are many collections of medical instruments used by naval surgeons. We mention some of them -- they are quite extensive:
1. Opthalmic instruments of 1930-1939, which all battleships carried.
2. Superb collections of medical instruments from the Engllsh, German and Japanese navies of WW I and WW II, with others going back to the 18th and 19th centuries.
3. There are also many pathology specimens, and displays of tattooing and its dangers. Also some excellent natural history and fossil collections.

Everything in the museum is immaculate, and lovingly cared for by Mr. Tom Parsons, a former Petty Officer in the Royal Navy. The museum is of great interest, and Mr. Parsons very knowledgeable. He will tell you many interesting historical facts -- some with a sigh, such as the abolition in 1970 of the Royal Navy's daily "rum ration"! This was due to the "exacting demands" of the "technical navy."

Hempstead (Essex)
Location - 38 miles north of London, and about 20 miles south of Cambridge.
Train - From London (Liverpool Street) to Saffron Waldon, and then by taxi to Hempstead.
Road - Take the A11 towards Cambridge, but turn right on the A1063 to Saffron Waldon. At Saffron Waldon take the B1053 to Radwinter and Hempstead.

Hempstead, Essex, is a small village in lovely countryside, but of particular interest because it is here that William Harvey (see also under Folkestone, London and Padua, Italy) is buried, and the village has a long association with the Harvey family.

The importance of William Harvey has been described under Folkestone, his birthplace, so suffice it to say that it is here in Hempstead that his body lies in the very old Parish Church of St. Andrew. The reason for this is that Harvey had no permanent home, but often visited his brother Eliab's home, Wincelow Hall, about a mile from the church. Wincelow Hall was burned to the ground in the 19th century, only the servants' quarters surviving, and a new house has been built on the site of the old. In any case Harvey's tomb is in the Harvey Chapel of St. Andrew's Church, and is in very good condition, having recently been restored by the Royal College of Physicians, with which Harvey was so closely associated most of his life. Harvey lies in the center of the chapel in a large sarcophagus made from a single block of Carrara marble. It is very impressive and a fitting resting place for this distinguished man. In a vault beneath the church there lie 49 of Harvey's relatives in plain lead coffins. The vault can only be seen by permission of the vicar, but if the church is open there is no difficulty in seeing the Harvey Chapel.

KEW (Surrey)
Location - 10 miles west and slightly south of London.
Train - Take the London Underground's District Line (towards Richmond) from Victoria or Earls Court and get off at Kew Gardens.
Road - From London take the A4 to the west and turn off along the A307 to Kew (just where the A4 joins the M4). In the summer it is also possible to go from London to Kew by riverboat on the Thames.

Kew, Surrey, is the home of the Royal Botanic Gardens, which may be said, without any exaggeration, to be the foremost botanical gardens in the world.

The Royal Botanic Gardens
Kew Road
Kew

Phone - 01-940-1171
Opening hours:
Gardens, 10.00 - dusk.
Glasshouses, 11.00 - dusk.
Small charge for admission.
Extensive literature available at the "Orangery."

No nation in the western world has such a long and continuous gardening tradition as Britain. Going back 2000 years to Roman times, advances in gardening have been virtually unbroken, and it is a pleasure to record that from the great Royal Palaces and country estates of the nobility, to the smallest cottage and urban house, British gardening is still alive and flourishing! For over two centuries, no place has had more importance in the development of modern gardening, scientific botany, and all the glories that derive from them, than the Royal Botanic Gardens at Kew (commonly referred to as "Kew Gardens"). Just as Down House in Kent is the "Mecca" for all biologists, so also is Kew the "Mecca" for all gardeners and botanists.

The origins of the gardens go back to the beginning of the 18th century, when the land on which they are now situated was part of the Richmond and Kew estates of King George II and Queen Caroline. Their son Frederick, Prince of Wales, lived on a part of the estate which now comprises Kew Green. He died in 1751, but in 1759 his widow, Augusta, the mother of King George III, started a small botanic garden within the area of the present gardens. On the death of George II, and later Princess Augusta, the entire estate became the property of George III. In a farsighted act, the King put the supervision of the gardens under the brilliant and much traveled botanist, Sir Joseph Banks (1743-1820), and it was Sir Joseph who set the high standards and determined the future scientific nature of the gardens. Sir Joseph was also very influential in having plants collected from all over the world and brought back to Kew. On his death, the gardens went into a period of decline, but in 1841 they became the property of the state, and are now under the direction of the Ministry of Agriculture, Fisheries and Food. At the same time they were handed over to the state, Sir William Jackson Hooker (see later) became their first director, and he not only revived them but expanded their scientific functions far beyond what Sir Joseph Banks had envisioned. In due course more land and facilities were given to the gardens by Queen Victoria and Edward VII, and at present they comprise an area of about 300 acres. To maintain this and provide the services for the many functions of Kew, there is a scientific staff of about 150, and a total staff of over 600. Also in 1965 the Wakehurst Place estate of over 400 acres at Ardingly, Sussex (see under Ardingly) came under the direction of Kew. On his death in 1865, Sir William Jackson Hooker was succeeded as director by his son, Sir Joseph Dalton Hooker (see later), and this brilliant botanical father and son were responsible for the modern

51

preeminence of the gardens. It is pertinent therefore that we give here a short biography of each of these outstanding botanists.

William Jackson Hooker (1785-1865) was born at Norwich, and received a good education, which included drawing, so necessary to botanists. Very early in life he exhibited an intense interest in animals and plants, and before he was twenty he had discovered a new British moss. Soon afterwards he was illustrating some of the major botanical books of the day. In 1809 he went on an expedition to Iceland, where he botanized extensively. However, on the way home his ship caught fire, and Hooker barely escaped with his life. But all his specimens were lost! (Some years later the same fate was to overtake Alfred Russel Wallace.) Nevertheless, Hooker managed to publish his journal of the expedition in 1811. Through the influence of a friend and patron, Dawson Turner, Hooker bought an interest in the Turner family brewery, which gave him a secure income so that he could devote his full time to botany, and in 1815 married Maria Turner, his patron's eldest daughter. However, the brewery did not prosper as well as expected, and in 1820 Hooker took up the post of Regius Professor of Botany at Glasgow University (see under Glasgow). There he had a very productive 20 years, during which he wrote many botanical books and articles, and also immeasurably improved the botanic gardens. So conspicuous were his services to botany, that he was knighted in 1836, and in 1841 was appointed director of Kew. It was made clear that the object of this appointment was for Hooker to turn the embryonic and decaying gardens into a national botanic garden of the first rank. In fact, he far exceeded every expectation. It is not necessary to elaborate here all the innovations and expansions he made, suffice it to say that all the major research functions of the gardens were established under him, as well as a library, herbarium (the nucleus of which was his own extensive herbarium) and the Museum of Economic Botany. As a result of his prestige, enthusiasm and influence in high places, plants from all over the world flowed into Kew. Despite his enormous administrative duties he still continued to write and illustrate botanical books. In 1855 his son Joseph Dalton Hooker became his assistant, and upon Sir William's death at Kew in 1865, his son succeeded him as director.

Joseph Dalton Hooker (1817-1911) was born at Halesworth, Suffolk, the second child of Sir William Jackson Hooker (see above). From the earliest age his father's influence on his upbringing, education and indeed his whole life was predominant, and above all else was his interest in botany. At 18 he published his first botanical paper and at age 22 he received his MD degree from Glasgow University, where his father was Professor of Botany. In the same year (1839), and not long after Charles Darwin had returned from his voyage in H.M.S. Beagle, young Joseph Hooker received an appointment as assistant surgeon and naturalist on H.M.S. Erebus, sailing under the command of Captain James Ross on a four year voyage to Antartica, the Falkland Islands, Tasmania, New Zealand and Australia. During his voyage of discovery (Hooker was to go on many more), he was an ardent botanizer, much of it on virgin ground, and in due course his work was published in six huge volumes under the title "The Botany of the Antarctic Voyage of H.M. Discovery Ships Erebus and Terror." With this he at once became one of the leading botanists of the world. On his return from the voyage of the Erebus in 1843, Joseph established himself at Kew, where his father had become director, and also established his lifelong friendship with Charles Darwin. The subsequent careers of the two men were closely intertwined, indeed they became each other's mentors, and "testing grounds" for the ideas and theories which their active minds poured forth.

In 1847 Hooker set off again on a long voyage of discovery this time to India, and later to the Himalayas, Sikkim and Nepal. His botanizing on this journey, was if anything, more productive than the previous ones, and in due course his work was published in many volumes. It is of great interest that it was during this journey that Hooker collected so many species of Himalayan rhododendrons, which were sent back to Kew and have since been propagated all over the world. It is also of great interest that his "Himalayan Journals" (dedicated to Charles Darwin) are one of the classics of travel books, and can be enjoyed by all. On a personal note, Hooker was married in 1851 to Frances Harriet Henslow, the daughter of the Cambridge botanist, the Reverend John Stevens Henslow, who had such an influence on Charles Darwin. She died in 1874, and two years later he was married again to Hyacinth Symonds. Both marriages were extremely happy and there were many children.

In 1855 he became assistant director to his father at Kew, and succeeded him as director in 1865. Under his directorship, Kew became the modern, research oriented, botanical institute that it is today, serving botanists on a world-wide basis. Despite his day to day responsibilities at Kew, Hooker undertook many more botanizing travels to such places as Syria and Palestine, Morocco, the Canary Islands and North America. With all this his books and monographs continued to grow in number. He became the foremost botanist of his time, and was duly knighted by Queen Victoria for his abundant services. He died in 1911, at the age of 94.

It will be obvious to our readers that Kew and the Hookers are almost synonymous, but we will now describe in more detail some of the fascinating and vitally important scientific aspects of Kew, which derive in large part from one or the other of the Hookers.

The most obvious part of Kew Gardens is of course the extensive living collections within the 300 acres. While the sheer beauty and size of the gardens may overwhelm the visitor (and there is always something in bloom at Kew!), we must never forget that their primary function is not to serve as a public park, but as a scientific institution dedicated to the advancement of botany in all its varied aspects. Behind the beauty, and the obvious meticulous care of the living collections, botanical research is the overriding concern. To give an idea of the extensiveness and variety of the living collections, we will simply list some of the main ones: grass and bamboo gardens; rose and iris gardens; birch, poplar, willow, oak, alder, ash, conifer, Rosaceae, walnut, mulberry and Leguminoseae collections; rhododendron, azalea, magnolia, lilac, wisteria and forsythia gardens; winter-flowering shrubs of many kinds; aquatic gardens; rock gardens and many more. In addition, there are the numerous glasshouses specializing in tropical rain forest plants, ferns, succulents, alpine plants, palms, tropical water lilies, Australian plants and many others. Suffice it to say that the interested visitor can spend many days, preferably spaced over different times of the year, simply savoring the glories of the living collections.

The herbarium is situated just a few yards outside the main gate and across the square behind some rather fine iron railings. The herbarium is not open to the public on a regular basis, but you can ask permission to see it, and if an appropriate person is available they are usually obliging. It can only be used by outside persons with special permission. At present it comprises a complex of four wings surrounding a courtyard, except for a "break" to permit entry of fire engines! The library (see later) is also housed in this complex. The herbarium was founded in 1852 on a small scale, but in 1854 and 1867 the extensive private herbaria of George Bentham and Sir William Hooker were added, and these formed the basis of the modern herbarium which now comprises over 5,000,000 specimens, and is certainly one of the largest and most important in the world. The two "old" (19th century) wings are really very

54

beautiful "period pieces" of architecture, with their balconies, superb open spiral staircases and glass skylights. In each, there is a ground floor and two upper balcony floors. The cabinets are all made of white pine (*Pinus strobus*), which would be prohibitive in cost today! The two newer wings are of 20th century origin and reflect a more utilitarian attitude.

The functions of the herbarium are based on the "Hooker days" when they prepared floras of the British Empire. Today it is a research herbarium for world flora, and also serves botanists throughout the world. They specialize in the flora of Britain, Australia, New Zealand, South Africa, India, Tropical Africa, the West Indies and South America. They are constantly engaged in preparing floras of these and other places throughout the world. Much of it is done on contract for the newer nations. Their special collections include those of Sir Joseph Dalton Hooker, and his original drawings (botanists and herbarium people in particular must be good artists-- it is part of careful observing!), John Lindley's orchid herbarium, many collections of early African explorers, and even some specimens collected from the famous (or infamous?) voyage of the Bounty. The herbarium has many other functions, but we will just mention one more, and that is to publish, in cooperation with the library, the "Index Kewensis". This was the idea of Charles Darwin and Sir Joseph Dalton Hooker, and consists of nothing less than a listing and description of all flowering plants ever discovered throughout the world! Needless to say it is constantly updated as new plants are discovered, and old ones reclassified. In closing this short description of the herbarium and its functions, we can only say that no words of praise, for the past and present, are too great for this unsurpassed scientific botanical institute.

The library of Kew (located in the herbarium complex) is both historically and functionally closely associated with the herbarium. It is not open to the public, but the visitor may ask to see it, and like the herbarium staff they are obliging if someone's time is available. The library can only be used by obtaining special permission from the librarian. Founded in 1852, it became a major botanical library, with the acquisition in 1854 of George Bentham's library and in 1867 Sir William Hooker's library. Since then it has constantly expanded, and now contains over 150,000 volumes, being particularly rich in pre-Linnean botanical works, and floras of the world. Many of their historical items are unique and priceless. The function of the library is to serve the research staff at Kew and botanists throughout the world.

The library is housed in a new wing and consists of three sections:
1. The Archives Room, which is a magnificent long gallery, where the main working collections are housed.
2. The Travels and Maps Room which houses the records of many of the early botanizers throughout the world.
3. The Kewensia Room. This houses all the various papers, letters, drawings, notes, etc. of Sir William and Sir Joseph Dalton Hooker.

The library also contains many other interesting items too numerous to mention. It is pleasant to record that it is today in the hands of a very knowledgeable and dedicated staff.

The Jodrell Laboratory (just inside the Jodrell Gate off Kew Road) is Kew's principle laboratory of basic research into the way in which plants function and have evolved. Founded in 1876 by Sir Joseph Dalton Hooker (with funds provided by his friend Thomas Phillips-Jodrell), it quickly became one of the leading botanical research institutes in the world and remains so today. With over 100 years of active research, and the publication of that research, its record can be described as constantly being in the forefront of botanical research, with great contributions to botany. Today it specializes in plant anatomy, biochemistry, biochemical systematics and cytogenetics. The plant physiology section has recently been moved to Wakehurst Place (see under Ardingly).

Opposite the front entrance of the Jodrell Laboratory is a large systematic garden of herbaceous plants. Arranged in easily comparable families, there are over 2000 species represented in this garden. This supplies marvelous facilities for evolutionists, and also helps students and the public to understand the range of variation among herbaceous plants. These are wild plants, not cultivated for decoration. In addition, this garden is rapidly becoming a major place for the preservation of endangered species. The systematic garden with its carefully labeled plants is a gold mine of interest for the botanically minded. One may wander freely (for hours!) around the garden, but the staff requests that you touch nothing -- there is no need for it anyway.

In addition to all this, there are several botanical museums at Kew, which are fascinating and very instructive.

The General Museum (open to the public), which is opposite the Palm House at the other end of "The Pond," is basically a museum of economic botany, and after seeing it one cannot help being impressed more than ever by our utter dependence on plants. Some of the displays vividly illustrate the history of agriculture and gardening, the origins of crop plants, the cultivation of domestic plants, and the breeding of domestic plants, the use of wood in buildings, furniture and art, including musical instruments, the making of paper and many more. This is a marvelous aesthetic and educational museum.

The Wood Museum, located between the main gate and the Jodrell Laboratory, is also open to the public, and displays a variety of woods and their uses, also craftsmanship in wood. Many people today appreciate the beauty of wood, and this is an excellent place to see many of its uses.

The Marianne North Gallery (open to the public) is located opposite the Temperate House near Kew Road, halfway between the Lion and Victorian Gates. Marianne North (1830-1890) was born in Hastings, the daughter of a middle-class family (her father was MP for Hastings), and from the earliest age she exhibited a talent for drawing and painting. However, she never had any formal training in art. This did not deter her, and managing in one way or another to escape the inhibiting social restraints placed on a woman of the Victorian age, she travelled alone all over the world, painting flowers in their natural habitat. Among the places she visited for this purpose were North America, Jamaica, Brazil, Japan, the East Indies, Ceylon, Australia, New Zealand and Chile. Her output was enormous, and 848 of her paintings are preserved and on display in the Marianne North Gallery. It is a remarkable collection.

The Orangery is slightly to the left off the Broad Walk upon entering at the main gates. It is the information center for Kew, but in addition it houses a small art gallery, temporary exhibits of current interest, and a pictorial exhibit of the history and functions of Kew. There are also excellent bookstalls specializing in works on botany and horticulture.

In addition to all we have mentioned here, there are many unseen functions performed by the staff of the Royal Botanic Gardens at Kew. These include the quarantining of plants for introduction from and to foreign lands, the training of horticulturalists (a degree from Kew is much prized!), conserving endangered species, and perhaps most important of all the giving of expert professional advice on all matters botanical to governments and institutions all over the world.

There is one last thing we must mention at Kew, and that is the Parish Church of St. Anne, located on Kew Green a short distance before reaching the main gates of the gardens. This is a fascinating old church, where over the years some very famous people have worshipped, including five Queens of England, Victoria, Alexandria (wife of Edward VII), Mary (wife of George V), Elizabeth (wife of George VI) and Elizabeth II. This is commemorated by specially hand embroidered kneeling cushions in the front pew. However, just as interesting to us, is that the botanic trio, Sir Joseph Banks, Sir William Jackson Hooker and Sir Joseph Dalton Hooker were all members of the church and worshipped there. This is commemorated in the church by plaques in their memory and also the handmade kneeling cushions. There is also one of the latter in memory of Marianne North. Both Sir William and Sir Joseph Hooker are buried in the churchyard. This church might be described as "the botanists' church". The Parish Church of St. Anne is only open at certain times (due to the danger of vandalism), but it is worth the effort to try to see it.

In concluding our section on the Royal Botanic Gardens at Kew, we can only say that the visitor is not likely to be disappointed. Furthermore, there is always something new in botany at Kew.

LONDON

London, situated astride the Thames near its mouth, is one of the major cities of the world and the capital of the United Kingdom. Its history goes back well beyond Roman times (it was known to the latter as Londinium), and today it consists of a vast complex of boroughs and towns all incorporated into what is known as Greater London. This is the place where almost all visitors to Britain will quickly establish themselves for longer or shorter periods, as it is not only the transportation hub of the country, but the variety of events and things to see, both social and cultural, as well as those of historical interest are, in our opinion, unsurpassed in the world. In no sense can we attempt to give a selection of these, all we can advise is that visitors read a good guide book, get a good map, and try to familiarize themselves as quickly as possible with the excellent public transportation, underground trains (commonly known as "the tube" or "the underground"), buses and taxis. Of course, none of these beat walking if you really want to know and see London! It will perhaps be of help to say that almost everything the visitor is likely to want to see is north of the Thames or immediately on the south bank. From the biological and medical perspective, London has long been the major center for these in Britain and thus there is a great deal to see.

British Museum of Natural History
Cromwell Road (Corner of Exhibition Road)
South Kensington
London, SW7 2DD

Phone - 01-589-6323
Opening hours:
        Weekdays 10.00 - 18.00
        Sundays 14.40 - 18.00
        Closed on some national holidays.
        No charge for admission.
Underground - South Kensington

This is one of the finest natural history museums of the world, and while it is administered by the main British Museum in Great Russell Street, Bloomsbury (see under British Library), its location is quite different. It is convenient and useful to mention here the fact that there are three other major museums in the immediate area of the Natural History Museum. The first of these is the Victoria and Albert Museum (open the same times as the Natural History Museum, but closed Fridays). Located on the opposite corner to the Natural History Museum, with entrance on Cromwell Road, it is one of the great art (both fine and applied) museums of the world, and in addition it often has special exhibits of great interest. Secondly, there is the Science Museum (see below) on Exhibition Road, and next door to it the Geological Museum (see below).

In its present form the Natural History Museum dates from 1860, when it was decided to split off the natural history section of the British Museum, which was founded by an Act of Parliament in 1753. However, the present building housing the Natural History Museum, was not opened until 1881. Even today the building is impressive for its architecture and size. In 1975 a huge new wing was added to house their 7,000,000 specimens of fossils.

The primary functions of the museum are both education and research, and its main funding comes from the British Government. It would be hard to overestimate the importance of the Natural History Museum in the development of our knowledge and understanding of all living things. The size of the operation alone tells part of the story, for they employ 300 scientists and possess over 40,000,000 specimens! Some of these come from the famous voyages of Captain Cook, the voyage of Charles Darwin in the Beagle, and many others, but most from much more recent expeditions. The main aspect of the museum's research is taxonomic, that is, the identification and classification of all animals and plants, and it is a main reference point for biologists all over the world.

Magnificent statues of Charles Darwin (1809-1882) and Thomas Henry Huxley (1825-1895) in the north hall of the main rotunda set the tone for the whole thrust of the museum's research and displays. This is the basic idea that all life on this earth has evolved by means of natural selection, and the public galleries reflect this theme. The museum has five subdivisions, Zoology, Botany, Palaeontology and Anthropology (combined), Entomology and Mineralogy. There is also a section of Ornithology, but this is located at Tring, Hertfordshire (see under Tring). All the subdivisions are well represented in the public displays in the galleries. These galleries are rapidly being renovated from their basic Victorian designs, to reflect the more modern aspects of biology such as ecology, diversity, behavior and life processes. One of these new exhibitions, entitled "Human Biology--An Exhibition of Ourselves" was opened in 1977, and others have followed rapidly. Thus although a hundred years old, the Natural History Museum has no intention of losing its paramount role and position in biology.

As one would expect of such an institution, it has a library to match its huge operations. The library is only open to the public by special permission of the librarian. There are in fact five libraries which reflect and serve the functions of the main subdivisions of the museum. We need hardly add that their collections are extensive and priceless.

Science Museum
Exhibtion Road
South Kensington
London, SW72DD

Phone - 01-589-3456
Opening hours:
      Weekdays 10.00 - 18.00
      Sundays 14.30-18.00
      Closed on some national holidays.
      No charge for admission.
Underground - South Kensington.

      The Science Museum is primarily a museum of the physical sciences and technology, but in 1981 there was added the Wellcome Museum of the History of Medicine. The museum contains a superb collection of optical instruments, including a microscope (c. 1675) said to have belonged to Robert Hooke (1635-1703), a pioneer in microscopy, and the first person to describe a plant cell. There are doubts about this however, but if it is not one of Hooke's, it is certainly a replica of one, and came from the royal collection of George III. George III was a prolific collector, and most of his collections have in due course found their way into various British museums.

      It was always somewhat amazing to us that a country like Britain, with its long tradition of excellence in medicine and also so historically oriented, did not have a good medical museum. But with the establishment of the Wellcome Museum of the History of Medicine this is fortunately no longer the case. We hesitate to say this medical museum is the best in the world, because they are all different, but it is certainly the largest, and second to none. The Wellcome Museum occupies the fourth and fifth floors of the Science Museum, and consists of 43 huge dioramas and reconstructions on the fourth floor, depicting the history of medicine from neolithic times to the present, while on the fifth floor are over 500 display cases, all in chronological order, on virtually every aspect of the history of medicine. They are beautifully displayed and explained. Almost all this vast collection comes from Sir Henry Wellcome F.R.S. (1853-1936), one of the founders of the pharmaceutical house of Burrows and Wellcome. Sir Henry was born in the United States, but as a young man he took out British citizenship and in due course became very wealthy and devoted 40 years of his life to collecting. In addition to his collections in the science museum, he also founded the Wellcome Institute of the History of Medicine (see below). Certainly no one has ever done more for the history of medicine.

We simply cannot imagine anyone, with an interest in the history of medicine, going to London and not taking time to see the Wellcome Museum of the History of Medicine. Allow at least 3 hours!

Geological Museum
Exhibition Road
South Kensington
London, SW72DD

Phone - 01-589-3444
Opening hous:
     Weekdays 10.00 - 18.00
     Sundays 14.30 - 18.00
     Closed on some national holidays.
     No charge for admission.
Underground - South Kensington.

The Geological Museum is next door to the Science Museum. It is actually part of the Institute of Geological Sciences, with world wide ramifications in geological research. Many of the impressive displays are being modernized, and their exhibit on "The Story of the Earth" can only be described as unsurpassed. It is beautiful and very educational. Their library, which is open to the public, is primarily a research library for geologists, and they have a superb collection of early geological books.

The "museum complex," consisting of the British Museum of Natural History, the Science Museum, the Geological Museum, and the Victoria and Albert Museum, is an incredible concentration of history and displays of great interest, but it is also a center of active research. The visitor can spend may profitable and enjoyable days around the corner of Cromwell Road and Exhibition Road in South Kensington.

The Linnean Society of London
Burlington House
Piccadilly
London

Phone - 01-734-1040
Opening hours:
> Normal business hours.
> Admission by appointment only.
> Children are not admitted.

Underground - Green Park.

The Linnean Society of London was founded in 1788 with the primary function of promoting natural history throughout the world. In its 200 years of existence it has remained true to that goal, and has played an enormous role in the development of our knowledge of natural history. During the time since its inception almost all great British naturalists (and many non-British ones also) have been elected Fellows, and include such names as Sir Joseph Banks, Sir Joseph Dalton Hooker, Charles Darwin and Alfred Russel Wallace. Of great interest also is the fact that it was at a meeting of the Linnean Society in 1858 that the original paper on evolutionary theory by Charles Darwin and Alfred Russel Wallace was read.

The society of course derives its name from the great Swedish botanist, Carl Linnaeus (1707-1778), whose importance to scientific botany can scarcely be overrated, and we will give a short biography of him under Uppsala, Sweden (see Uppsala, Sweden). Here we will stick to the society itself, which is famous not only for its achievements in natural history, but also for the fact that it has come to be the resting place of most of Carl Linnaeus' collections of plants, animals, manuscripts, correspondence, books, etc., and these are still a major reference source for biologists throughout the world. It is of great interst as to how the collections came into the hands of the Linnean Society. When Linnaeus died in Uppsala in 1778, his son Carl inherited his father's library and his collections, except for his priceless herbarium. This went to his widow Sara, and unfortunately was not well cared for. Young Carl died in 1783, just 5 years after his father, and all his father's collections then went to his mother. Linnaeus had warned his wife before his death that his collections would increase in value with time. However, in 1783 she needed money, and unable to find a Swedish buyer she sold them for about £1000 to an English medical student and naturalist, James Edward Smith. In the following year 1784, he shipped them to

London. Needless to say the Swedes were very upset about this, but in a sense they had no one but themselves to blame. The collections remained in Smith's hands until his death, when they passed to Smith's wife, but in 1829 the Linnean Society bought them from her for a little over £3000, with the express purpose in mind that they should be permanently available to scientific workers. The collections today are more or less intact as from the time of purchase, except for Linnaeus' medical books, which were returned to Sweden in 1892. This has perhaps been offset by the subsequent addition of many valuable botanical works.

The Linnean collections are housed in a special strong room, where temperature and humidity are carefully controlled, and it is a pleasure to record the excellent condition they are in, as well as the professional care they are accorded. It is not treated as a museum, but as a research collection, and scholars from all over the world come to study and consult it. In addition to this, there is the magnificent library of the society, which is both a working and historical library. With over 100,000 volumes, it is one of the major biological libraries of the world. It can only be used by the society's 1500 Fellows, and by scholars who have the permission of the librarian. Other priceless possessions include the herbarium of Sir James Edward Smith (the founder of the society), and many busts and portraits of famous naturalists, Fellows, etc., including the original and huge portrait of Charles Darwin by John Collier.

On the far side of the courtyard behind Burlington House are the premises of the National Academy of Art, and it was here in the right hand wing (facing the building) that the famous Darwin/Wallace paper was first read in 1858.

We can only describe the Linnean Society as a "biological gem" particularly from a historical point of view.

The British Dental Association
63/64 Wimpole Street
London W1

Phone - 01-935-0875
Opening Hours:
      Monday-Friday 10.00 - 16.00
      No charge for admission.
Underground - Oxford Circus.

The British Dental Association is the main professional society of British dentistry, having as its main function the general advancement of dentistry in the United Kingdom. Founded in 1880, it is over 100 years old, and has played a huge role in the progress of modern dentistry.

The offices and facilities of the British Dental Association on Wimpole Street are really for the benefit and use of professionals in the field. However, there are two things there that the biologically-oriented visitor will find of great interest. The first of these is the Dental Museum and it is certainly one of the best dental museums in the world. It displays graphically the advance of dentistry from the earliest times to the present day, and it is especially good in that it is being kept up-to-date on a year-to-year basis. In addition to the superb collection of dental instruments (some of them grim!) covering the last three centuries, they have displayed dental chairs, cabinets, anaesthetic equipment, etc., and a great collection of old dental cartoons, many with a merciless humor! We have nothing but praise for this museum, which the visitor will find fascinating. Secondly, and in the same building, is their superb dental library. This is not open, as such, to the public, but you may ask to see it, and we found the librarians obliging and cooperative. This is certainly one of the great dental libraries in the world. It is both working and historical, and from a historical point of view it is probably the best and most complete.

The Royal College of Physicians of London
11 St. Andrew Place
London NW1

Phone - 01-935-1174
Opening Hours:
    Monday-Friday 10.00 - 17.00
    No charge for admission.
Underground - Great Portland Street

The Royal College of Physicians of London is over 400 years old. It has engaged in a whole variety of activities in its long history, and as such has had, and continues to have, an enormous influence on British medicine.

It was founded in 1518 by charter from King Henry VIII. At this time it became obvious that the medical standards of physicians in England were well below those on the continent, particulary those of Italy, and Henry VIII's charter was an attempt to remedy this situation. Since that time the college has played a major role in British medicine, which has spread to much of the rest of the world.

One of its early Fellows was no less a person than William Harvey (see under Folkestone and Hempstead) who added enormous prestige to the college. Today the Royal College of Physicians of London is chiefly responsible for the maintenance and improvement of the standards of physicians in Britain.

Of main interest to the visitor is their historical medical library, which while not open to the public, nevertheless has a "main reading room," and this is open to the public. From time to time in this room there are magnificent displays of early medical works. In the college also are a series of fine portraits of their famous Fellows, including one of William Harvey.

The John Snow Public House
39 Broadwick Street (corner of Lexington Street)
London W1

Phone - 01-437-1344
Opening Hours:
    Normal Pub hours.
    No charge for admission.
Underground - Piccadilly Circus.

There is no more pleasant place in London for the medical historian that the John Snow Pub! Why is the John Snow Pub of historical significance? The answer is that a great medical discovery took place near where the pub now stands, and it was a Dr. John Snow who was responsible for it. John Snow (1813-1858) should, in our opinion, have greater status in the history of medicine than is normally accorded to him, because he made major contributions in both anaestheiology and epidemiology.

Born in York, (see under York), the son of a farmer, he is said to have been a good student, and at the age of fourteen was apprenticed to a surgeon. In his teenage years he became a temperance advocate and for the rest of his life he practiced this himself. It is perhaps ironic that he should be commemorated by a pub! Also, very early in life he had to cope with cholera epidemics, on which he became very knowledgeable. In 1836 he migrated to London, and in 1844 he received a medical degree from the University of London. When the anaesthetic, ether, was introduced from the United States in 1846, Snow at once recognized its potential, and within one year he had invented a reliable apparatus for its administration, and published a book on it entitled "On Ether."

In the same year, 1847, James Young Simpson (see under Edinburgh) introduced chloroform, and Snow embraced this also, but recognized the differences between this and ether. He quickly became the leading authority on anaesthesia, so much so, that he was chosen to administer chloroform to Queen Victoria in 1853 at the birth of Prince Leopold. He later (1858) published another book entitled "On Chloroform."

However, in the meantime he had not lost interest in cholera and its means of spreading. This was of course long before the theory of the microbial origins of disease, as put forth by Pasteur (see under France). As early as 1849 Snow believed and publicly said so, that cholera was "water borne" but, it was not until 1854 that he was able to prove this. In that year there was a terrible outbreak of cholera in Soho, which was the area in which Snow himself lived. So severe was the outbreak, that over 200 people died within 3 days. Suspecting that the disease was "water borne," Snow did a study of the incidence of the disease in relation to a public well on Broadwick Street, and noticed that the closer people lived to the well the greater the incidence of cholera. He also noticed that a sewer pipe passed within a few feet of the well, and believed that this was the source of contamination of the well water. Accordingly, Snow advised the authorities to "remove the handle from the pump!" Despite much protest, this was in due course done, and the cholera stopped at once. While the microbial origin of the disease was not understood for many years to come, the "water borne" nature of it was, and with the sanitation reforms which quickly followed, cholera virtually disappeared from the British scene. Furthermore, the understanding of the value of clean water in general gave rise to enormous improvements in health.

Dr. John Snow never married and died at the early age of 45. Nevertheless his contributions to medicine and human welfare remain secure for all time.

After Snow's death in 1858, London expanded rapidly. In due course a public house was built on or near the site of the former well. Some 20 years ago, a group of historically-minded London doctors asked the brewing company (Watneys), who owned the pub, if they could put up a plaque on the pub commemorating Dr. John Snow and his great discovery. Watneys was delighted, and at the same time renamed the pub the "John Snow," and there it stands today as a reminder of this great man. Inside the pub are a variety of framed photographs and documents commemorating Snow's great discovery. It is popular with the local people and a nice "cosy place" to have a drink (or a "pub lunch"), and to toast Dr. John Snow!

The Royal Society of London
6 Carlton House Terrace
London SW1

Phone - 01-839-5561
Opening Hours:
     Normal business hours.
     No charge for admission.
     Not suitable for children.
Underground - Charing Cross or Piccadilly Circus.

The Royal Society is one of the oldest scientific institutions in the world, with origins as far back as 1645, but in 1662, King Charles II, who had previously become a member, granted the first charter. Thus, it has been in existence for well over three centuries, and has played an enormous role in the advancement of science. In its original charter granted by Charles II, the purpose of the society is stated to be "the promotion of natural knowledge." Using modern English we would describe this today as the promotion of the natural sciences, and throughout its history the society has remained true to this end. Today it accomplishes this by a variety of means. These include the maintenance of the highest scientific standards in the electing of its Fellows, the awarding of medals, lectureships, and research grants, the publishing of newly discovered knowledge, promoting cooperative scientific research throughout the world, the giving of scientific advice to the government and other bodies, and finally maintaining a historical scientific library. The society also maintains a remarkable collection of paintings and busts of its former Fellows, whose names include Robert Boyle, William Harvey, Sir Isaac Newton, Sir Joseph Banks, John Hunter, Charles Darwin, Sir Joseph Dalton Hooker, Joseph Lord Lister, and many more. In fact, virtually every truly great British scientist has been a fellow of the society since the latter part of the seventeenth century.

The Royal Society is of course an active working organization, and is not generally open to the public. However, they are remarkably cooperative with really interested people, and will show them around if an appropriate guide is available. In addition, their scientific meetings are held on Thursdays from November to June, and these are open to the public.

If a visitor is fortunate enough to get a tour of the premises, he should, in our opinion, ask particularly to see three things: the library, the portraits and busts of the Fellows, and the Council Room. The library, which is such a major part of the Royal Society, has a historical collection of scientific books almost beyond praise! The preservation of such works by the Society is considered a vital part of our culture. The library also preserves their own publications and those of their Fellows. Their collections of portraits and busts are scatered in various rooms and hallways of the premises, but most can be seen with the help of a guide. Finally of special interest is the Council Room, where they not only have portraits of their distinguished Fellows, but some huge and magnificent tapestries woven by the Zulu Tribes of Africa.

The Royal Society of London is a remarkable institution, and its influence on the development of all science has been, and continues to be, enormous.

The Wellcome Institute of the History of Medicine
Wellcome House
183 Euston Road
London NW1

Phone - 01-387-4688
Opening Hours:
      Normal business hours.
      No charge for admission.
Underground - Euston Square.

The Wellcome Institute of the History of Medicine has probably done more to preserve our medical heritage than any other organization. Its origins go back to the pharmaceutical company of Burroughs and Wellcome, which in 1895 became the sole property of Henry Wellcome (1853-1936). Henry Wellcome, a very wealthy man, had wide interests in such things as archaeology, medical education, medical research and most important for us the history of medicine. He made enormous collections in the latter area during his lifetime, and these are now housed in the Science Museum (see previously).

When Sir Henry Wellcome died in 1936, his will set up the Wellcome Trust, a part of which is the Wellcome Institute of the History of Medicine. This is centered at 183 Euston Road, and comprises an Academic Unit which is associated with the University of London, a superb historical library, and a museum of various aspects of the history of medicine. Still at Wellcome House (and there are no plans to move it), is the Museum of Medical Science. It is a technical medical museum, with heavy emphasis on tropical medicine. In the building also are old apothecary shops, reassembled intact, and a fine art collection. These may be seen upon request at the director's office.

In addition to all this, the academic staff of the Wellcome Institute of the History of Medicine is an active research unit, whose function is to promote the history of medicine in a whole variety of ways.

The Royal College of Surgeons of England
Lincoln's Inn Fields
London

Phone - 01-405-3474
Opening hours:
>Normal business hours.
>No charge for admission.
>Children are not admitted.
Underground - Holborn.

The Royal College of Surgeons, which incorporates the Hunterian Museum, was established in its modern form in 1800. It was based then, as now, on the humanitarianism, educational concepts and professionalism which John Hunter (1728-1793) established as the blueprint for medical training, and which became the subsequent pattern followed by medical schools in both Britain and the United States. The major function of the Royal College of Surgeons can be summed up by saying that it is to maintain and improve the standards of surgery in all their varied aspects and it has played an enormous and world wide role in these respects. It is an entirely autonomous body, all of their funds coming from their Fellows and public subscriptions, but none from the government.

It is important to note that the college, including its magnificent Hunterian Museum, is an active working organization, and is not open to the general public. However, it is open to members of the medical and allied professions, medical students and members of scientific societies. Other individuals and groups must make application to the curator of the Hunterian Museum. The Hunterian Museum is neither a natural history museum, nor a museum of medical history. Visitors require some basic knowledge of biology to appreciate it. It is not suitable for children and they are not allowed.

Having said all this, we will add that the curator and the porter in charge at the front desk are generally cooperative. But they have responsibilities to the institution they serve, and the public must respect these.

John Hunter (see also under East Kilbride) can figuratively be described as the "Patron-Saint" of the Royal College of Surgeons. Just as his famous brother William Hunter (see under East Kilbride) established obstetrics as a medical science, so also did John put surgery into a scientific category rather than a "butchery procedure" practiced largely by barbers and other untrained people. He eventually became surgeon-extraordinary to King George III and in 1783 established his own medical school in what is now Leicester Square. Here the student had to undergo rigorous training, study animal and human specimens, attend lectures and practical classes, and do research. All the things we now take for granted in medical training. Honors poured in upon him, and over 1000 of his students spread his ideas and methods throughout the modern world. He died in 1793, probably from syphilis, with which he inoculated himself in order to distinguish it from gonorrhea. Dedication!--but unfortunately the experiment failed into the bargain! He is buried in Westminster Abbey.

By far the most important exhibit at the Royal College of Surgeons is the Hunterian Museum. Originally, Hunter's collection comprised about 14,000 specimens, but time, and above all the World War II bombing of the college have reduced the number considerably. Nevertheless, there are still many thousands left and they are magnificently displayed in this lovely and fascinating museum. All the more remarkable when one realizes that most of it is the work of one man and the specimens are 200 years old! Within the displays are dissections illustrating all the main basic structures and functions of the animal form. These include the endoskeleton, joints, muscular systems, nervous system, organs of special sense, integumentary system, organs of locomotion, the digestive, circulatory, respiratory, excretory and reproductive systems, as well as ductless glands. One is immediately struck by the incredible skill of the dissections. Guide books to the museum are available, and there are also many other interesting publications on sale. The staff is dedicated, enthusiastic and helpful. All in all, a visit to the Hunterian Museum is a thrilling experience.

The Royal College of Surgeons also has a superb collection of the medical instruments of Joseph Lord Lister (see under Glasgow), many of which are on display in the lobby and can easily be seen.

There is also a large statue of John Hunter which dominates the lobby, and there are lovely original portraits by Sir Joshua Reynolds and others. The library of the college (which can only be seen by special permission) is one of the great medical libraries of the world, with priceless holdings, including all Hunter's publications, and most of his case books. Regrettably, his manuscripts are mostly lost.

Finally let us point out that in the central part of Lincoln's Inn Fields, on the Kingsway side near where Sardinia Street enters, there is a new and lovely mounted bust of John Hunter.

St. Thomas' Hospital
Lambeth Palace Road
London SE1

Phone - 01-928-9292
Opening Hours:
    Normal business hours.
    No charge for admission.
Underground - Waterloo.

St. Thomas' Hospital is one of many major hospitals in London, but from our point of view it has the distinction of being indelibly associated with Florence Nightingale (1820-1910) (see also under Middle Claydon, East Wellow, Aldershot, and Kaiserswerth, Germany) who did so much to found the modern profession of nursing.

The origins of St. Thomas' go back to the 13th century, but it has only been in its present location since 1871, and is now a vast and ever expanding hospital. With all its varied history and contributions, no aspect has proven more far reaching than the founding in 1860 at St. Thomas' of the Nightingale Training School for Nurses. With its foundation, modern nursing may be said to have begun. It is difficult for us today to realize that right down to the middle of the 19th century, to be a nurse was a social disgrace. It was in fact tantamount to being a prostitute, and many women combined the two professions. However, a new course was set by Florence Nightingale. Most of the early probationers (called "Nightingales" then as now!) scattered to all parts of the earth and spread their knowledge, expertise and dedication. Thus modern nursing was born, and is today a totally vital and indispensable part of medicine--something rather easily overlooked by many people, including doctors themselves.

The background of Florence Nightingale is not only of interest, but has great historical importance from which we can all learn. She was born in Florence, Italy (hence her name) in 1820. Her English parents, both wealthy and upper class, were at the time of her birth, living in Italy. However, at the age of one she accompanied her parents back to England to live at the family home of Embley Park (see under East Wellow), and it was there that she spent most of her childhood. By all accounts she was a highly intelligent and motivated child, and loved to learn. She received the education thought suitable for an upper class woman of her day, designed to make her a wife and mother, but very little else. As she grew her family expected her to lead a glittering social life, but she was in great conflict with this. Her early inclinations were clear when she was only 20. At that time there was a famine in the area where she lived, and she immediately plunged herself into social work. Her happiness at doing something constructive was obvious to all, and at the same time she announced her intention of becoming a nurse. Her parents were horrified, and ordered her to give up the whole idea, but their remonstrations proved useless. However, it was to be another 13 years before she actually broke the parental bonds and left home. In later life she came to have nothing but contempt for her mother and sister. "They have nothing to do" she said "but tell each other not to get tired putting flowers into water!" In the meantime, she traveled to Rome, and there she met Sydney Herbert, who was destined to become a very influential British politician, and was responsible for getting a lot of Florence Nightingale's ideas put into practice. On returning to England she had a love affair with a certain Richard Monckton Milnes but it did not last, and in fact she never married. She also visited the Institute of Lutheran Deaconesses at Kaiserswerth, Germany. Here she spent six months studying their methods of nursing. She was impressed with the organization of the hospital, but thought little of their sanitation and nursing care. From Kaiserswerth she went to Paris, and studied in the hospitals under the authority of the Sisters of St. Vincent de Paul. On her return to England again, her parents were more adamant than ever against her desire for a career in nursing, but finally in 1853 at the age of 33 she left home and started to work at the Governesses' Sanatorium on Harley Street, London. This did not last long, as events simply overtook her.

In 1853 the Crimea War started. Britain and France supposedly went to protect Turkey against Russian attack. Things went badly for Britain from a military point of view, and the London Times reporter on the spot dispatched home articles criticizing the incompetencies and indifference of the generals and other authorities to the suffering of soldiers, particularly those sick or wounded in the hospital. This had a profound and far reaching effect in England. Sydney Herbert was at this time Minister at War, and in due course Florence Nightingale and about 20 nurses were sent out to Scutari in Turkey, where the main hospital was located. The authorities were hostile! But by her patience, high standards, organizational ability and leadership, she eventually reconciled the army to nurses. In a short time there were heavy casualties, and the doctors and generals in desperation turned to her for help, and her moment of triumph had arrived. Her degree of dedication and leadership soon spread far and wide. She never asked her nurses to do anything she didn't do herself. For example, during one winter at the Scutari Hospital, she personally was present at the death of over 2000 soldiers.

In 1855 the situation got even worse, and at one point there were more soldiers in the hospital (12,000) than in the trenches (11,000). The death rate was appalling, and eventually a sanitary commission was sent out from London. Florence Nightingale became personally responsible for implementing their reports, and in a short time the death rate dropped from 40% to 2%! Somewhat inevitably, however, she got ill herself, but did not return to England until 1857 after the end of the war. England had prepared a great welcome for her, but she would accept no personal acclaim, and immediately started a campaign for reform in sanitation, health care, hospital care and nursing, which included the founding of the Nightingale Training School at St. Thomas'. The rest of her long life was devoted to these ends. During these later years of her life, she also wrote a great deal on nursing, hospital design and sanitation. Her "Notes on Nursing" published in 1859 (the same year as Darwin's Origin of Species!) is considered a classic on the subject, and there were many more.

All biographers of Florence Nightingale agree that "she was not an easy person to get on with" - reformers seldom are! However, her influence was enormous. Basically she brought about three revolutions. The first of these was in the profession of nursing itself, which she raised from a very low status to one of high social (if not monetary) regard. Secondly, she brought about a revolution in hospital administration and design. But thirdly, and perhaps the most important of all, was her social revolution. She, more than anyone else, broke the Victorian tradition that the only thing young, well-educated women could do was to become homemakers and have children. Thus, she was a great social liberator, whose impact is still with us today. She died at her London home on South Street in 1910 at the age of ninety. Prior to her death, and true to her nature, she refused a national funeral and burial in Westminster Abbey. Instead she was buried in the family grave within the churchyard of East Wellow, Hampshire (see under East Wellow).

At the present time there is no central place in St. Thomas' (or anywhere else), where the belongings of Florence Nightingale are assembled. However, as part of a current extension to one of their buildings it is hoped that there will be a "Florence Nightingale Museum," where most of her surviving things will be properly displayed (a drive for funds is already underway). In the meantime we must recognize that her former possessions are scattered and in order to see them we will have to rely on the cooperation and courtesy of those responsible for their preservation. First of all, there is a very impressive statue of Florence Nightingale on the east balcony, not of the original cast, because the latter was stolen some years ago and has never been traced. However, the firm who did the casting in the 19th century was traced, and by good fortune they still had the original mould! So the present statue is as near to the original as possible. It may be seen by any interested visitor.

In the office complex of the District Nursing Officer, there is a variety of furniture which formerly belonged to Florence Nightingale. These include her piano, desk and several chairs. There are also other small items, prints and even clothes. Similarly in the office complex of the Nursing Personnel Officer there are such items as Florence Nightingale's medicine and needlework chests, another desk, books, etc. There is also a lamp of the type used by nurses in the Crimea, but it probably did not belong to Florence Nightingale. All these things can only be seen by the permission of the appropriate Nursing Officer. They are busy people, but one can ask, and they are helpful.

The Nightingale Training School for Nurses adjoins St. Thomas' Hospital on the east side. It is a modern building, but of particular interest to us is the fact that in their library are many of the books from Miss Nightingale's own library, including her Bible--she was incidentally a devoutly religious woman, and like St. Joan of Arc, believed she had had a mystical experience as a young woman. The library also has copies of all the books she wrote. However, her private papers are held by the Archives Department of the Greater London Council, which is right next door to St. Thomas'. The library holdings of the Nightingale Training School may be seen with the permission of the librarian. In addition to all these interesting

75

aspects of St. Thomas', it is convenient to note here that during the years Florence Nightingale was associated with the hospital, she lived in a house on South Street. The house itself no longer survives, but there is a ceramic plaque put up by the London County Council to commemorate this. To reach the site, take the underground to Green Park and then walk up Park Lane beyond the Dorchester Hotel to South Street and turn right. Her house was at what is now 8-10 South Street, and the plaque reads:

in a house
on this site
Florence Nightingale (1820-1910)
lived and died

A simple tribute to this great human benefactor.

Old St. Thomas' Hospital Operating Theatre
c/o The Chapter House, Guy's Hospital
St. Thomas Street
London

Phone - 01-407-7600
Opening Hours:
      Variable - phone for information.
      Small charge for admission.
Underground - London Bridge.

      This is the second oldest surviving operating theater in the world. It dates from 1822, and was originally the women's operating theater of St. Thomas' Hospital, but is now part of Guy's Hospital and is maintained as a museum. It is a remarkable, though somewhat "grim" place, but at the same time a historical "gem," and we cannot recommend too highly a visit here to see what the "realities" of surgery were only 150 years ago. When we were last there (1985) the responsible officer in charge was Mr. M. Fellows-Freeman (ext. 3149) and the curator was Mrs. Jean Miller. Literature is available at the entrance desk.

      The origins of this operating theater go back to the 18th century, when the loft of the church was used by the apothecary of St. Thomas' Hospital, for drying, storing and preparing the medicinal plants used by the hospital. For this reason it was actually called "the herb garret." In 1822, a new women's operating theater was built in the garret, as part of the space occupied by the apothecary and his herbs. The theater was in use for 40 years until 1862, when St. Thomas' Hospital sold its property to the railway company using nearby London Bridge Station, and in 1865 the hospital moved from the area altogether. The Operating Theatre, although abandoned, was fortunately bricked-up and this no doubt saved it from complete decay. It remained that way until 1956 when, in the course of renovations, it was discovered and fortunately its value recognized. It took many years of careful work to restore it to its original condition, but with funds provided mainly by St. Thomas' and Guy's Hospitals and the Wolfson and Wellcome Foundations, the work was completed, and it and the adjoining herb garret were opened to the public in 1962.

On entering the theater, one is struck by the fact that virtually everything was made of wood, in contrast to the stainless steel in a modern operating theater. But to us at least, the most striking thing of all is to realize that "these walls must have seen and heard some terrible things." When it opened in 1822 anaesthesia was unknown, and it was not until 1847 that anaesthesia was first used here. Secondly, throughout its entire 40 years of use, no techniques of antisepsis were in use. It was entirely pre-Listerian (see under Glasgow). This is attested to by the fact that in one corner of the room is a china basin and jug used by the surgeon to wash up after the operation! In fact, the contents and whole atmosphere remind one dramatically of three necessary preliminaries before modern surgery became possible. These are the placing of surgery on a scientific basis, mainly by John Hunter (see under the Royal College of Surgeons) in the later 18th century, the introduction of anaesthesia in the late eighteen sixties, and also asepsis. Thus, this Old Operating Theatre is a vivid and very educational reminder of the history of this part of medicine. The herb garret adjoining the theater is now a historical medical museum, thanks largely to the work of the late Mr. R.J. Scott, who for many years lovingly cared for everything as curator. There are very interesting displays in the herb garret, including some of the original poppy seed used to supply opium.

In concluding this section on the Old St. Thomas' Hospital Operating Theatre and Herb Garret, we feel obliged to say that a visit to them should be "a must" for anyone interested in medical or human history.

St. Mary's Hospital Medical School
Praed Street (corner of Norfolk Place)
Paddington
London, W2

Phone - 01-262-1280
Opening Hours:
    Normal business hours.
    No charge for admission.
Underground - Paddington.

St. Mary's Hospital is relatively new in comparison to other London hospitals, having only opened its doors in 1851, and the Medical School attached to it was founded in 1854. However, its fame has rapidly become second to none, because it was here in 1928 that Alexander Fleming (1881-1955) first observed the antibacterial properties of the mold, *Penicillium notatum*, though it was many years after this before the active agent "penicillin" was extracted, purified and became clinically available. Nevertheless, we may correctly say that with Fleming's discovery the "antibiotic age" was born, and it is no exaggeration to say that it has proved to be the greatest therapeutic advance in all the history of medicine. It is safe to say also that without penicillin and subsequent antibiotics, one third of the people in the world today would not be alive.

Alexander Fleming was a Scotsman, having been born in Lockfield, Ayrshire in 1881. He was brought up on the family farm receiving an average education for a rural community, and by the time he was 13 he was already in London where he worked at a variety of jobs. An important turning point in his life came when at the age of 20 he inherited a small amount of money and decided to use it to study medicine. Accordingly, he entered St. Mary's Hospital Medical School, and apart from a stint in the Army in the first World War, he remained with St. Mary's for the rest of his working life.

Early in his career, Fleming became interested in the study of the antibacterial mechanisms of the body, and also antibacterial agents, but he never attempted any massive survey of potential antibacterial agents as did Paul Ehrlich (see under Frankfurt, Germany). In fact, it was really a chance event which led him to what is now called penicillin therapy. In 1928 while working in his laboratory at St. Mary's he noticed that some colonies of staphylococci on a culture plate had been destroyed by an accidental contamination of a mold which had literally floated in through the window of his laboratory! Fortunately, Fleming had "a prepared mind" and recognized the significance of this event. The mold, subsequently identified as *Penicillium notatum*, was found to inhibit the growth of many other species of pathogenic bacteria. In the following year, 1929, he reported his findings to the London Medical Society, and also published a short paper entitled "On the Antibacterial Action of Cultures of a Penicillium," and suggested its use for antibacterial therapy. However, at that time chemical techniques were very inadequate, and extracts of the active substance (penicillin) were impure and their effects unpredictable. Despite his efforts, and those he enlisted for help, the problem could not be solved, but Fleming never lost hope that sometime in the future the problem of extracing a pure sample of penicillin would become a reality. This indeed occurred in Oxford in 1940 when Ernst Chain (1906-1979) and Howard Florey (1898-1968) (see under Oxford) accomplished this. The following year, 1941, the first clinical trial was made on an Oxford policeman, who was dying of a severe bone disease due to an infection. The infection was immediately arrested and the patient started to improve at once. Unfortunately, there was only enough penicillin available for five days of treatment, and after this the infection took over again and the patient died. This was an unhappy beginning, but subsequent trials confirmed that the results of penicillin therapy could be almost miraculous. Fleming himself was overjoyed at this turn of events. In 1941 England had long been at war, and was shortly to be joined by the United States. Fortunately, the authorities in both countries were persuaded of the importance of this discovery, and the highest priority was given to the difficult task of the extraction of penicillin in meaningful amounts. Spurred on by ever increasing war casualties, the problem was in fact solved in a remarkably short period of time, thus a new era of medical therapy was ushered in. At first penicillin was only available to the allied armed services, but with the coming of peace in 1945 its use quickly spread throughout the world, and its originator, Alexander Fleming, was hailed far and wide as a hero. Honors poured in upon him from all over the earth. He was knighted by King George VI in 1944 (as were Florey and Chain), and he, Florey and Chain all received the Nobel Prize in 1945.

Fleming's first wife, Sarah Marion McElroy, died in 1949 leaving him a lonely man. In 1953 he was married for the second time to Dr. Amalia Coutsouris-Voureka, a Greek scientist who was working at St. Mary's. Tragically, they were only to have two years of married life, for Sir Alexander died suddenly in 1955. His body was cremated, but his ashes are preserved in St. Paul's Cathedral (see under St. Paul's Cathedral). In concluding this short biography of Sir Alexander Fleming, it is perhaps in the interest of accuracy to say that many scientists and historians of medicine find fault with Fleming for "not doing the right experiments" after his first observations in 1928, and also for lack of perseverance. Be that as it may, and remembering the old saying that "hindsight is easy," the fact remains that it was Fleming's careful observations and deductions that were instrumental in bringing about this enormous advance in medicine.

Unfortunately, the authorities at St. Mary's Hospital Medical School have not seen fit to preserve much of the associations of Sir Alexander Fleming. His laboratory has been so altered and put to new uses, that for practical purposes it no longer exists and is now an office complex. In spite of this, there are two things worthwhile seeing. The first of these is a very nice plaque on the side of the Medical School building just to the left of the main entrance on Praed Street. It reads as follows:

Sir
Alexander Fleming
1881-1955
Discovered Penicillin
in the second story
room above this plaque.

It is an interesting experience to look up at the second story window above the plaque, and realize it was here that antibiotic therapy, which is such a major aspect of medicine today, had its beginnings. Secondly there is the library and conference room on the third floor of the Wright-Fleming Institute (part of the Medical School). This is not open to the public, but the visitor may ask permission to see it from the librarian of the Medical School. Some of Fleming's personal library is in this room, and it was the library he used in his day. In this room also is a nice portrait of him and a bust. Most of Fleming's library, his notes and records, laboratory equipment, etc. are scattered and generally inaccessible except to professionals, and even then it is difficult! The house in Chelsea in which Sir Alexander Fleming lived for many years still stands. It is at 20 Danvers Street. To reach it take the underground to Sloane Square, and then walk down Kings Road to Paultons Square (it is quite a step!), and turn left. This then leads into Danvers Street. The house is privately occupied, and is not marked in any way.

We find it a pity that more of the materials and associations of this great human benefactor are not preserved and available for viewing by the public. Perhaps in the future there may be a "Fleming Museum"-- we hope so.

Westminster Abbey
Parliament Square
Westminster
London SW1

Phone - 01-222-5152
Opening hours:
>Open to the public most days, so long as there is no service or special event in progress.
>Photography in the Abbey is forbidden except by special permission.
>No charge for admission.
Underground - Westminster.

Westminster Abbey is more to Britain than simply a church. It is in fact a national shrine where, throughout the ages, many of her great sons and daughters have been buried or commemorated, and these include biologists and doctors.

There are many things in Westminster Abbey of great historical interest and beauty, but we strongly recommend some knowledge of British history before a visit there, as well as the use of the official guide book. We will confine ourselves here to memorials of the great scientists. There is a booklet available entitled "The Abbey Scientists," which we recommend. On entering the Abbey by the West Door, the Nave is straight ahead, and almost immediately in the center of this is the memorial to Sir Winston Churchill and the tomb of Britain's Unknown Soldier. To the left of this is the North Aisle, and within the floor of this aisle are the tombs of John Hunter and Charles Darwin. Nearby are the tombs of Sir Charles Lyell (1797-1875), the geologist and close friend of Charles Darwin, and the great physicist Michael Faraday (1791-1867) and others. Further on in the North Transept is the memorial to Sir James Young Simpson, and in the South Transept, as part of "poet's corner," is the memorial to Stephen Hales. Westminster Abbey is a fascinating place, where the visitor can spend many enjoyable hours, but none of them better than seeing the memorials to famous British scientists.

St. Paul's Cathedral
Ludgate Hill
London, EC4

Phone - 01 - 248 - 2705
Opening hours:
>Open to the public most days, so long as there is no service or special event in progress.
>No charge for admission.

Underground - St. Paul's.

St. Paul's Cathedral, like Westminster Abbey, is somewhat of a national shrine, and it is here that the ashes of Sir Alexander Fleming are interred. They are in the crypt underneath the main floor, and are located in a wall not far from the tomb of the Duke of Wellington. There is a plaque on the wall indicating the location of his ashes. It is worth a visit by those interested in the contribution of this great man to medicine and human welfare.

Brompton Cemetery
Fulham Road
London, SW10

Phone - 01-352-1201
Opening hours:
>Daily 9.00 - dusk.
>No charge for admission.

Underground - West Brompton.

Here in this cemetery Dr. John Snow (see under The John Snow Public House) is buried. To find the grave, go through the entrance off Old Brompton Road. Turn left at the first cross walkway inside the cemetery, and the grave is about 30 yards along on the right. It is easily seen. The burial register number is 18588, and it is officially described as being on North Walk, Compartment E, Location 52. It is inscribed:

To
John Snow, M.D.
Born at York
March 15th, 1813
Died in London
June 16th 1858
In remembrance of his great labours in science and of the
excellence of his private life and character, this monument with the
assent of Dr. William Snow has been erected over his grave by his
professional brethren and friends.

Restored in 1895 by Sir Benjamin W. Richard F.R.S.
and a few surviving friends.

The grave has been restored three times: Firstly in 1895 by Sir
Benjamin W. Richardson. Secondly in 1938 by anaesthetists from
Britain and the United States. It was destroyed by a German bomb in
April 1941 -- but restored for the third time in 1951 by the
Association of Anaesthetists of Great Britain and Ireland, who now
maintain it.

The British Library
The British Museum
Great Russell Street
London, WC1

Phone - 01- 636 - 1544
Opening hours:
     Weekdays, 10.00 - 17.00
     Sundays,   14.30 - 18.00
     No charge for admission.
Underground - Tottenham Court Road.

The British Library is one of the truly great libraries of the
world, and has played an incalculable role in the development of all
human knowledge. It was founded by Act of Parliament in 1973,
and can now be described as the National Library of Britain. At the
present time it is in a state of transition, with three main operation
divisions. These are the Reference Division, the Lending Division,
and Bibliographic Services. It is the Reference Division with which
we will be concerned here, because it comprises the former library
departments of the British Museum, including the Science
Reference Library, which are still housed there.

83

The origins of the British Museum are of great interest. It was founded by Act of Parliament in 1753, with the object of bringing together the enormous collections of Sir Robert Colton, as well as those of the First and Second Earls of Oxford and those of Sir Hans Sloane. Included in the Act were specific provisions for a library, and the money to buy these collections was raised by a government-sponsored lottery! Fortunately, it worked well. Just four years later in 1757 the library was greatly enhanced by the presentation of the entire Royal Library of King George II (1683-1760), which contained the collections of every British King since Edward IV (1442-1483). It was certainly then, and fortunately still is, one of the most priceless collections to survive the ravages of time. The collections were enhanced again in 1823, when King George IV (1762-1830) presented to the Museum the library of his father King George III (1738-1820). Thus in its early years the library was greatly helped by gifts from Royalty. At its foundation the British Museum Library was established as a "copyright library," which under the law (going back to the Press Licensing Act of 1662) entitles it to a free copy of every book published in the United Kingdom. Its holdings are now well over 10,000,000 and include historically important manuscripts, documents, maps, letters, etc.

The Reference Division of the British Library (formerly the British Museum Library) is not a library for the general public or for causal use. Nevertheless, qualified scholars may obtain permission from the librarian to use it, if their need is considered justified. However, any visitor may see the famous "Reading Room" and we can assure you it is worth a visit. This magnificent and huge domed room, with its surrounding bookstacks, was designed by the architect Sydney Smirke and opened in 1857. It has been in continuous use ever since, and its value to the advancement of scientific knowledge is incalculable. The dome of the building was damaged by a bomb in the early days of World War II, but fortunately no serious or permanent damage resulted.

To visit the Reading Room, it is only necessary to ask permission at the main entrance desk. However, visitors are only admitted every hour, on the hour, from 10.00 - 16.00. They cannot accommodate anyone between hours. In addition to the Reading Room, there is of course the rest of the museum with its magnificent heritage of cultural exhibits.

The Freud Museum
20 Maresfield Gardens
Hampstead
London, NW3 5SX

Phone - 01 - 435 - 2002
Opening hours:
      Weekdays, 10.00-17.00
      Sundays,   13.00-17.00
      Closed - Christmas, Boxing and New Year's days.
      Small charge for admission.
Underground - Finchley Road.
      On leaving the station, cross Finchley Road and walk south to
      Trinity Walk and turn up this to Maresfield Gardens.

This was the home of Sigmund Freud (see under Vienna, Austria) after he had to leave his native Austria because of Nazi persecution. He lived here for one year only from 1938 until his death in 1939. After he died the house became the property of his daughter Dr. Anna Freud, who lived there until her death in 1982. Upon her death the house and its contents came under the control of "The Sigmund Freud Archives," and is now open as a museum. The house is easily recognized by a plaque on the outside erected by the London County Council, which reads:

Sigmund Freud
1856-1939
Founder of Psychoanalysis
Lived here in
1938-1939

Within the museum, left much as Freud knew his house, is his furniture, including his "famous couch" which was brought from Vienna, his priceless anthropological and antiquarian collections, as well as his personal library which contains all his works in both the German and English editions. Also many other items associated with Freud and the history of psychoanalysis. In addition the museum contains various meeting rooms, and carries on many educational and research activities.

Not far away in the grounds of the Hampstead Public Library at 88 Avenue Road, (underground Swiss Cottage) is a very fine statue of Sigmund Freud sculptured by Oscar Nemon.

Finally the ashes of Sigmund Freud, his wife and their daughter, Dr. Anna Freud, are all in The Golders Green Crematorium, Hoop Lane, Hampstead. The underground is Golders Green, and the crematorium is open daily 9.00 - 17.00. The office (phone 01 - 455 - 2374) is open Monday - Friday 9.00 - 17.00.

Hampstead Cemetery
Fortune Green Road
London

Opening hours:
        Daily, 9.00 - dusk.
        No admission charge.
Underground - West Hampstead.

This is the cemetery where Joseph Lord Lister (see under Glasgow and Edinburgh) is buried. It is sometimes referred to as the West Hampstead Cemetery, simply because it is located in West Hampstead, but there is in fact only one cemetery in Hampstead. The cemetery is about a 15 minute walk from the underground station (alternately one can take a taxi). The grave of Lord Lister and his wife is in section WA, and the number is 432. If you enter the cemetery at the main gate, the grave is located at the bottom of the cemetery to the left of the chapel, and is on the left side of a minor walkway. You do not have to go off the walkway to find it, it borders the walkway. It is a simple grave for this great man and his wife.

The Royal Horticultural Society
Vincent Square
London, SWI

Phone - 01 - 834 - 4333
Opening hours:
        Normal business hours.
        No charge for admission.
Underground - Victoria.

The Royal Horticultural Society was founded in 1804, with the basic function of promoting horticulture in all its varied forms (see later). Today it is one of the foremost botanical organizations in the world, and continues, with great success, its original function. While its offices and main library are in Vincent Square, its major gardens are at Wisley, Surrey (see under Wisley).

It is of great interest that the founder of the Royal Horticultural Society was John Wedgwood, the eldest son of Josiah Wedgwood, who established the famous pottery firm of that name. Another founding member was Sir Joseph Banks. John Wedgwood made it clear how he envisioned the Society: "the object," he said, "of this Society shall be to collect every information respecting the culture and treatment of all plants and trees, as well as culinary and ornamental." Despite some terrible periods in its long history, it is remarkable how well the society has achieved that goal. Within a very few years, gardens and a library were established. In 1809 the society was granted a Royal Charter from King George III, and in 1821 the society persuaded the Admiralty to allow its nominees to sail on survey ships and bring back to Britain plants from all over the world. Of great significance also was that as early as 1830 (and long before most other institutions) women were elected as Fellows, and ever since have played a major role in the affairs of the society.

The worst period of the society's history was during the mid-nineteenth century, when it got into severe financial difficulties, one of the results of which was that its magnificent library was sold at auction. This included original hand drawings of flowers, many of them of Chinese origin. Fortunately, this period of disaster did not last long, thanks mainly to the interest and patronage of Queen Victoria, her Consort Prince Albert, and later King Edward VII. Of great importance also was the acquisition in 1866 of the personal botanical library of Dr. John Lindley, a Fellow of the society, and this became the nucleus of the present library. During the rest of the nineteenth century, the society grew by leaps and bounds, and by the time they celebrated their centenary in 1904, they were already in their new quarters in Vincent Square. Even more important their gardens at Wisley had been established. From then until the present, the society has continued to grow and to further the cause of horticulture in a variety of ways, including the publishing of journals and books, and the sponsoring of horticultural exhibits, shows and competitions.

Apart from the Head Offices, and the large Horticultural Hall, the main thing to be seen in the Vincent Square buildings is the library, and it is open to the public with the permission of the librarian. Located in a lovely old panelled room, with glass fronted book cases, it is now basically a working library for horticulturalists from all over the world. However, their historical botanical collection is priceless. Of particular interest is their outstanding collection of virtually all the great herbals and floras going back to the Great Herbal of Peter Treveris, written in Old English, and published in 1526 --

only a century after printing was introduced into Britain! If the librarians have the time available they are only too happy to show their collections to visitors, and the latter will not be disappointed. The library of the Royal Horticultural Society is of the utmost importance in the history of botany.

MAER (Staffordshire)
Location - 155 miles northwest of London, close to the town of Market Drayton.
Train - From London (Euston) to Stoke-on-Trent and then by taxi to Maer.
Road - From London take the M1 to the north, and transfer to the M6 just beyond Rugby. Follow the M6 around Birmingham as far as exit 12, and then follow the A5 to Shrewsbury. From Shrewsbury take the A49 north towards Whitchurch, but bear right onto the A53 towards Hodnet and Market Drayton. Follow the A53 around Market Drayton towards Newcastle - under - Lyme. About 7 miles out of Market Drayton take the A52 towards Stone, and within 1 mile along this road turn right to the village of Maer.

Maer, Staffordshire, is a small village set in the beautiful countryside of Western England, and what endears it to all biologists is that it was here in 1839 that Charles Darwin (see under Downe) married his beloved Emma Wedgwood. It was in this village that the Wedgwood family had their country residence, called Maer Hall. Here, as a young man, Charles Darwin came from his home in Shrewsbury to shoot game, to consult his uncle, Josiah Wedgwood (Uncle Jos), and above all to court Josiah's daughter, Emma. Eventually, Charles and Emma were married in Maer's Parish Church of St. Peter in 1839. Fortunately both Maer Hall and the Parish Church still stand.

One enters Maer by a small road, and on the right is Maer Hall. Across the road, almost exactly opposite Maer Hall, is the Parish Church which is up on the top of a hill. Maer Hall is no longer in the hands of the Wedgwood family and is a private residence. However, it has been well preserved and is much the same as in the early part of the 19th century. Although one may not enter Maer Hall, it is possible to get two excellent views of it. It is best observed by following the road a short distance past Maer Hall and then turning right up another small road. From the side of this road one can look down across the fields and have a magnificent panoramic view of Maer Hall and its beautfiul grounds. A second view of it is also possible by climbing up the pathway to the church, and then looking down on the buildings and grounds.

Maer Church is reached by climbing up a short but steep pathway. The interior of the church has undergone some renovations since Darwin and the Wedgwoods knew it, but the exterior is exactly the same, as also are the churchyard and the pathway up which Charles and Emma walked on their wedding day. Visitors may see inside the church with the permission of the Vicar, and there is available a nice historical guide to the church. The marriage of Charles Darwin and Emma Wedgwood is recorded in the Church Register on January 19, 1839. Charles Darwin's signature is in a rather shaky hand, perhaps because it was a very cold day or that he was very nervous--or perhaps both! Also recorded in the Baptismal Register is the fact that four of their children (William, Elizabeth, Henrietta and George) were baptised in the church. It is of interest that the birth, death and marriage register of the church goes back to 1558. In addition, the graves of Josiah Wedgwood and his wife Elizabeth are easily seen in the churchyard.

All in all Maer is a beautiful and fascinating little village to all biologists and those interested in biological history.

MIDDLE CLAYDON (Buckinghamshire)
Location - 55 miles northwest of London.
Train - From London (Marylebone) to Aylesbury and then by bus or taxi to Middle Claydon.
Road - Take the A41 to Watford and Aylesbury. At Aylesbury branch onto the A413 to Winslow and Buckingham. Then take the well marked side roads to Steeple Claydon and Middle Claydon.

Claydon House
Middle Claydon
Buckinghamshire

Opening hours:
> April - October only.
> Daily, 14.00 - 18.00; closed Mondays and Fridays.
> Operated by the National Trust.
> Small charge for admission.

Claydon House has been the seat of the Verney family since 1620. During her life Florence Nightingale (see under London) spent a great deal of time here.

In 1858 Sir Harry Verney (the 2nd Baronet) was married to Miss Parthenope Nightingale, who became Lady Verney and the mistress of Claydon House. She was Florence Nightingale's eldest sister, and for many years after the marriage, Florence was a frequent visitor to Claydon. She had her own bedroom now called Miss Nightingale's room, and it is beautifully preserved. Many of her personal belongings are here. These include some of her letters, her plans for hospitals, part of her library, prints, nursing badges and some of her own furniture. There is also a portrait of her by W.B. Richmond which hangs over the fireplace, and also photographs of her. Throughout the house there are other reminders of Florence Nightingale's association with it.

Claydon House with its surrounding beautiful park land is a thrilling place to visit, and the association with it of Florence Nightingale makes it even more so.

OXFORD (Oxfordshire)
Location - 60 miles northwest of London
Train - From London (Paddington)
Road - Take the A40 to the north, which joins the M40 at Denham, and this leads straight into Oxford via Headington.

The city's name is derived from the two words "ox" and "ford," and it is located in a valley between the Thames and Cherwell rivers. There was apparently no Roman settlement there, though a Roman road ran nearby. There were certainly settlements by the 8th century A.D., and in 872 King Alfred (849-901) founded three seats of learning at Oxford, and these formed the nucleus of what was to become Oxford University. By the end of the 12th century the university was well established, and in 1248 University College was founded. Through the centuries many more have been added, and there are at present 34. Like Cambridge University (see Cambridge), Oxford is a federal structure, and all undergraduate students must belong to a college.

Oxford is not as rich as Cambridge (which was an offshoot from Oxford) in its scientific heritage, having been more clerically oriented, and there was always considerable opposition to science at Oxford. Nevertheless, in recent times science has flourished there, and there are places of considerable scientific interest.

The Main Botanic Garden
High Street
Oxford

Opening hours:
>   May - September - Weekdays, 8.30 - 17.00
>   Sundays, 10.00 - 12.00 and 14.00 - 18.00
>   October - April - Daily, 10.00 - 12.00 and 14.00 - 16.30
>   No charge for admission.

This was originally founded as a Physic Garden in 1621 and is the oldest in England. Today it is a major center of biological research. However, at the entrance to the Rose Garden, a very important medical discovery is commemorated. It was in Oxford, at a whole variety of places, that the very necessary work of extraction and purification of penicillin was accomplished before it could be used in a therapeuetic way (see under St. Mary's Hospital, London). This was done between 1939 - 1943, and the event is recorded on a stone slab. It was given by the Albert and Mary Lasker Foundation of New York, and the names of those responsible for this great achievement are carved on the stone. They are:

E.P. Abraham	E. Chain
C.M. Fletcher	H.W. Florey
U.E. Forey	A.D. Gardner
N.G. Heatley	M.A. Jennings
J. Orr-Ewing	A.G. Sanders

This botanic garden is a great place for the biologically oriented.

The Museum of the History of Science
Broad Street
Oxford

Opening hours:
>   Monday - Friday, 10.30 - 13.00 and 14.30 - 16.00
>   Small charge for admission.

The Museum is housed in the Old Ashmolean Building and was established in 1925 . It contains an unrivalled collection of early astronomical and mathematical instruments. Also instruments of physics, clocks and watches, chemical apparatus, etc. Of particular interest for biologists, is their extensive collection of early microscopes including a reconstruction of Robert Hooke's compound microscope built before 1665. Hooke's original microscope apparently does not survive, but this reconstruction is based on Hooke's own description in the book, Micrographia, published in 1665. There are also fine collections of early surgical and dental instruments, and many things relating to the history of pharmacy. Also on display is some of the apparatus used in the original extraction of pure penicillin, which was done in Oxford (see earlier). The museum has a magnificent historical library in science, and its staff is actively engaged in research into the history of science. All in all it is a great museum for the history of science.

The Genetic Garden
Science Area Laboratories
Oxford

Opening hours:
>Monday - Friday, 9.00 - 13.00 and 14.00 - 17.00
>No charge for admission.

The Genetic Garden is part of the Botany School of the university and is primarily a research garden, but the public are admitted at the above times only.

It is located on the northern edge of the Science Area Laboratories, which is the southern edge of the University Parks. It may be reached by walking along Keble Road, which leads off the Banbury Road, and then taking the footpath through the University Parks to the northern edge of the Science Area Laboratories. It is located between the Physiology/Biochemistry Building and the Astrophysics Building. Alternately it can be reached by entering the Science Area Laboratories from South Parks Road where it is joined by Mansfield Road. Then walk through the laboratory area to the gardens on the south edge of the University Parks.

The Genetic Garden was founded in 1954, and although only an acre in size it demonstrates the processes of evolution in flowering plants. It also demonstrates the mutations of chromosomes and genes, plastids and plasmagenes, and hence the origin of hybrids, chimaeras and the causes of variegation. It also shows the causes and consequences of fertility and sterility, the nature of breeding systems with sex and heterostyly and the actions of viruses. Finally, it provides the evidence for the origins of cultivated domestic plants and of new species in nature. The botanically minded visitor will not be disappointed in the Genetic Garden -- it is a "gem."

The Oxford University Museum
Parks Road at South Parks Road
Oxford

Opening hours:
Monday - Saturday, 10.00 - 16.00
Small charge for admission.

The Oxford University Museum is an active teaching and research unit in the areas of zoology, entomology, geology and mineralogy, and it houses large collections in all these areas.

The building was erected in 1855 and 1860, as an expression of the growing awareness of the natural sciences as an important area of learning. However, this was done over considerable opposition from many members of the university! The building itself is very imposing, and the main court, which houses their huge collection of vertebrate fossils, is a remarkable sight. Right around this court is a gallery with many other displays. It is of particular interest that it was in the Upper West Gallery on June 30, 1860, that the "great debate" took place between Bishop Samuel Wilberforce and Thomas Henry Huxley on the newly published "Origin of Species" by Charles Darwin. That debate had a profound effect on the future development of biology, and the fact that it was held here is commemorated by a plaque outside the area where it occurred. The exact room has been considerably altered since the debate, and now houses part of the ornithology collections. The Oxford Museum is a lovely place, with great interest for biologists and those concerned with the history of biology.

There are many other places of great interest in Oxford, which the guide books explain, but we would like to recommend just two. The superb Ashmolean Museum (Beaumont Street) with its extensive collections of Egyptian, Greek, Roman, Near East and Chinese antiquities. Also the world famous Blackwell's Book Store on Broad Street. In the basement it has a room the size of a tennis court!-devoted to academic subjects.

SHREWSBURY (Shropshire)

Location - 150 miles northwest of London on the borders of Wales.

Train - From London (Euston) direct.

Road - From London take the M1 to the north and transfer to the M6
just beyond Rugby. Follow the M6 around Birmingham as
far as exit 12, and then follow the A5 to Shrewsbury. On this
route the traffic is very heavy, as it goes through the
industrialized areas, and in our opinion should be avoided if
possible. We recommend taking the M40 towards Oxford
and then joining the A40 just before Oxford. Follow this
around Oxford on to Cheltenham, Gloucester and Ross-on-
Wye. At Ross-on Wye bear right onto the A49 to Hereford,
and follow this north to Leominster, Ludlow and Shrewsbury.
This is a lovely and interesting route.

Shrewsbury, Shropshire, has a history going back well over
1000 years, much of it being a story of conflict between the English
and Welsh. It is located in a horseshoe bend of the Severn river,
and today is a lovely and prosperous old town. However, for us its
chief importance is the fact that Charles Darwin (see under Downe)
was born here on February 12, 1809, and spent all his childhood in
the vicinity. He is by far Shrewsbury's most famous son, something
that the townspeople are happy to acknowledge and remind you of!

Charles Darwin's father, Dr. Robert Waring Darwin, came to
Shrewsbury in 1786 to set up his medical practice. Within 10 years
he was so prosperous that he bought the land and built the house,
now known as the Mount. This became the family home and it was
here that Charles Darwin was born and brought up. Fortunately the
Mount still stands within its own grounds. The Mount is located
over the Welsh Bridge on the north side of a road called the Mount,
which joins the A458 towards Welshpool. The gate into the
grounds of the Mount has two plaques, one stating that it was the
birthplace of Charles Darwin, the second stating that it is now the
property of the Inland Revenue Service. Actually it is owned by the
Ministry of the Environment and leased to the Inland Revenue
Service. It is perfectly alright to go through the gate and look around
the grounds and the exterior of the house, which has not been
altered since Darwin's day. It is indeed a thrilling experience to
realize that here young Charles played with his sisters and brothers
(there were 6 in the family) and it was from here that he set out in
due course for Edinburgh University and later Cambridge University.
Also it was to this home that he came in 1831, at the age of 22, to

say goodbye to his family before setting out on the Voyage of the Beagle.

In 1817 at the age of 8, Charles was sent to a day school run by a Unitarian Minister, the Rev. G. Case, at 13 Claremont Hill. This building, now a private residence, still stands and is only a short walk from "The Square" of the town. The following year Charles went to the famous Shrewsbury School, founded in 1551 by King Edward VI. It was in Charles' day, under the direction of Dr. Samuel Butler. The school is still in existence,but has now moved outside of Shrewsbuy. The exterior is much the same, but the interior greatly altered. It is located in Castle street (opposite the Castle), and an easy walk from the Old Market Hall in "The Square." Outside what was the main entrance to the school, now approached through a lovely small park, is a magnificent statue of Charles Darwin, which is inscribed at the base with the words: "Erected by the Shropshire Horticultural Society, 1897." Charles remained at Shrewsbury School until the age of 16, when he went to Edinburgh University.

There are all kinds of fascinating stories that the natives of Shrewsbury will tell you about Charles Darwin. He certainly was interested in natural things from a very early age, and a certain Mr. Cotton introduced young Charles to the mysteries of geology, and in particular to a well known unusual boulder in Shrewsbury known as "The Bellstone". This boulder is of glacial origin and had a profound effect on Charles' mind when he realized it had been transported there by an "iceberg"! The stone may still be seen. It is inside the entrance to Morris Hall, which is just off the Square. There are many other interesting things in the lovely old town of Shrewsbury, but fortunately the citizens have placed the memory of Charles Darwin at the top of their list.

TEDDINGTON (Middlesex)
Location - Southwest of central London near Kingston-on-Thames, but it is now a part of Greater London.
Train - From London (Waterloo) by suburban train.
Road - Complicated, and we would not recommend the visitor to drive.

Teddington is the last resting place of Stephen Hales (1677-1761), who was a very important person in the history of medicine and botany. He was the minister of the Parish Church of St. Mary in Teddington for 51 years, and during this time performed brilliant experiments in both animal and plant physiology.

Stephen Hales was born at Bekesbourne, Kent, of an old and prosperous Kentish family, but practically nothing is known of his childhood. In 1696, at the age of 19, he entered what is now Corpus Christi College, Cambridge, and in one capacity or another remained there until 1709, when he was ordained, and went to Teddington as the parish minister. When Hales entered Cambridge, the university was "basking in the glory" of Sir Isaac Newton, who left Cambridge the same year that Hales entered. However, Hales was one of those greatly impressed by the deductive logic of Newton's work, and as a result he took the opportunity of learning some physics and mathematics, which was to stand him in good stead later on. He also learned some natural history and did some early experiments on animals and plants. Amazingly enough, although his major work was yet to come, he was well enough thought of to be elected a Fellow of the Royal Society in 1717.

When Stephen Hales arrived in Teddington, he started his experiments on animals again. However, he soon gave it up, to use his own words "being discouraged by the disagreeableness of anatomical Dissections." He wished he could apply the same techniques to the study of sap in plants, but despaired of ever succeeding. Nevertheless, he persevered, and in due course his efforts were rewarded. To use his own words again "Having, after other means proved ineffectual, tyed a piece of bladder over the transverse cut of the stem, I found the force of the Sap did greatly extend the bladder; whence I concluded, that if a long glass Tube were fixed there in the same manner, as I had before done to the arteries of several living Animals, I should thereby obtain the real ascending force of the Sap in the Stem." So was born the science of plant physiology!   Hales took a long time to publish his classic work, but this was finally achieved in 1727 under the title "Statical Essays containing Vegetable Staticks: Or an Account of some Statical Experiments on the Sap of Vegetables."

Having finally been successful with his experiments on plants, he turned back again to animals, where he succeeded in cannulating both the arteries and veins of several animals (sheep, horses, and dogs), and accurately measured their respective blood pressures. This work was published more rapidly and appeared in 1731-33 under the title "Haemastatiks or an Account of some Hydraulick and Hydrostatical Experiments made on the Blood and Blood Vessels of Animals."   This was the first time blood pressure was ever recorded.

Of course during all this time his primary duties to his parish came first, and the records clearly indicate he did not neglect them.

In 1720 at the age of 43 he married Mary Newce, a parson's daughter, but the marriage ended a year later when she died, probably in childbirth. Stephen Hales was left a lonely man, and he never married again. He had an inquiring mind and was an indefatigable worker. Amongst his other achievements was the measurement of water loss by plants, and he related this to the water present in a given area of soil. He also measured the rate of growth of leaves and shoots, and investigated the influence of light on plants, and was the first to recognize that plants took in carbon dioxide from the air. In addition to measuring the blood pressure of animals, he computed the velocity of blood in the arteries, veins and capillaries, and made the very important discovery that the latter were subject to dilation and constriction, thus greatly affecting blood flow. His contributions to respiratory physiology were impressive, for he distinguished between free gases and the chemically combined forms, measured the size of the alveoli and calculated the surface area of the interior of a lung. He also invented the U tube manometer and measured intrathoracic pressures during normal and forced breathing. He was also a pioneer of public health, and developed a method of distilling fresh water from seawater, and for the preservation of meat and water on long voyages.

In Hales' later years his enormous achievements were recognized, and honors poured in upon him from all over the world. However, he still remained the minister of Teddington until his death in 1761. It is pleasant to record these honors were not confined to his lifetime, for even today the American Society of Plant Physiologists remembers him by making its annual "Stephen Hales Award." He also has a tree named after him, *Halesia,* a native of Georgia, with which Hales had close connections.

The Parish Church of St. Mary is recorded in the Doomsday Book, but it has been rebuilt and modified many times since then, and in the nineteen twenties underwent a complete internal renovation. It is hard to realize that in Hales' day Teddington was a lovely small village, and that he lived the life of a country parson. The church is open at varying times, depending on functions, but is locked most of the time due to the danger of vandalism. However, arrangements can usually be made to see it by applying (preferably in advance) to the vicar. Stephen Hales is buried at the base of the tower within the church. The inscription on his gravestone is almost completely obliterated with the inevitable wear and tear of over two centuries. However, at present (1986) it is being restored. Right above the grave on the wall of the tower is a plaque erected in

1911, which contains the words of the original inscription. It reads as follows:

Beneath is the grave of Stephen Hales
The epitaph now partly obliterated but
recovered from a record of 1795 is here
inscribed by the piety of certain botanists. A.D. 1911

Here is interred the Body of
STEPHEN HALES D.D.
Clerk of the Closet to the Princess of Wales,
who was Minister of this Parish 51 years.
He died the 4th of January 1761
in the 84th year of his age.

Behind the altar of the church are three beautiful stained glass windows, and one of these is dedicated to Hales with the inscription

Stephen Hales D.D. F.R.S
who was minister of this parish 51 years
he died the 4th of January 1761 age 84

In the records of the church are preserved some entries in the original handwriting of Hales.

It is really a very pleasant experience to visit this lovely old church, with which Stephen Hales was so closely associated, and we recommend it to all.

TRING (Hertfordshire)
Location - 33 miles northwest of London.
Train - There is no railway station in Tring but there are frequent buses from London.
Road - From London take the A1 as far Mill Hill, and then fork on to the A41 which leads through Berkhamstead to Tring.

Tring, Hertfordshire, is a pleasant country town, but in addition it is the home of the Tring Zoological Museum, which is primarily an ornithological museum (but with many other animals as well), and comes under the direction of the British Museum of Natural History (see under London).

Tring Zoological Museum
Akeman Street
Tring

Opening hours:
  Monday-Saturday, 10.00 - 17.00
  Sundays, 14.00 - 17.00
  No charge for admission.

The Tring Zoological Museum derives from the private collections of Lionel Walter, second Baron Rothschild. Born in 1868, Lord Rothschild was the eldest son of the famous banking family, and thus a very wealthy man. From the earliest age, he had a passion for natural history, and soon established his private museum at Tring. He employed professional curators, and was able to send out collectors to all parts of the earth. However, Lord Rothschild was no recluse with his collections, and in 1892 the museum was opened to the public. To give some idea of the size and importance of his operations, during the first 50 years of the museum's existence, its staff published 1700 scientific books and papers, and described more than 5000 new species of animals. They also established a vast library devoted to zoology. The quality of their work was such that the institution became world famous.

In 1932 some of Lord Rothschild's bird skins were sold to the American Musem of Natural History (see under New York). These supplied the nucleus of that institution's ornithological collections. Lord Rothschild died at Tring in 1937, and in his will he left all his collections and museum to the Trustees of the British Museum, on the condition that his museum become an annex of the British Museum of Natural History and remain a center of zoological research, which in this case is mainly bird anatomy, behavior, ecology and bird songs.

Lord Rothschild was probably one of the foremost patrons of natural history, and a visit to "his museum" at Tring is a thrilling experience for all those interested in biology and its history. It is also pleasant to realize that its contributions to biology have been enormous, and that this tradition is still carried on today in the form of active high quality research.

WISLEY (Surrey)
Location - 25 miles southwest of London.
Train - There is no station at Wisley. Take a bus from London to
Ripley, and then a taxi to Wisley.
Road - From London take the A3, and turn off near Ripley at the
clearly visible signs pointing to the gardens at Wisley.

Royal Horticultural Society's Gardens at Wisley
Wisley

Opening hours:
Monday - Saturday, 10.00- dusk
Sundays, 14.00 - 18.00
Small charge for admission

From a biological point of view the Royal Horticultural Society's
Gardens at Wisley are second in importance only to the Royal
Botanic Garden at Kew (see under Kew).
There were substantial gardens at Wisley long before the
present site came into the hands of the Royal Horticultural Society in
1903. In that year the owner of the land, Sir Thomas Hanbury, gave
it in trust to the society for "the Society to use and occupy the
Wisley Estate or such portion thereof as the Society may require for
the purpose of an experimental Garden and the Encouragement
and the Improvement of Scientific and Practical Horticulture in all its
branches." Since that time the society has remained true to the
charge of Sir Thomas Hanbury. In fact Wisley is a story of
phenomenal success and the gardens are at present popular and
thriving. Today they consist of over 200 acres beautifully planted
and cared for by its staff of about 170. There is an incredible array of
garden flowers and shrubs, and there is always something in bloom.
Also carried on at Wisley are trials of new varieties of flowers, fruits
and vegetables, and basic research in horticulture and botany. They
also train professional horticulturalists, and a diploma from Wisley is
much prized.
The library at Wisley is basically a small working library for their
staff, but in addition they have a priceless collection of "old floras."
These can be seen by requesting the permission of the librarian.
It is difficult to exaggerate the contributions to horticulture (so
vital to us all), of the Royal Horticultural Society's Gardens at Wisley.
Visitors are always welcome, and will not be disappointed. We can
only hope the gardens continue to prosper!

YORK (Yorkshire)
Location - 225 miles north of London.
Train - From London (King's Cross).
Road - Take the M1 or A1 north to York.

York is one of the oldest towns in England, famous for its Cathedral, and it is the seat of the Archbishop of York. But for us, more important still is that York was the birthplace of Dr. John Snow (see under London--the John Snow Public House). The event is commemorated by a plaque on the north wall of the new Viking Hotel in North Street on the bank of the river Ouse, which Snow would have known so well. The plaque reads:

To
the memory of
JOHN SNOW
1813-1858
Pioneer Anaesthetist
and Epidemiologist
Born near here

Also in York is the very interesting "Cholera Burial Ground" dating from 1832, and a grim reminder of the realities of life when Snow was a young man. It is located immediately opposite the entrance to the British Rail Station and the Royal York Hotel.

Chapter 2

FRANCE

The cultural achievements and traditions of France are second to none, and her legacy to science is in the top rank of all nations. In the physical sciences, the names of René Descartes (1596-1650), Antoine Laurent de Lavoisier (1743-1794), Le Marquis Pierre Simon de Laplace (1749-1827), André Marie Ampère (1775-1836), Pierre Berthelot (1827-1907), Antoine Henri Becquerel (1852-1908), Pierre Curie (1859-1906) and Marie Curie (1867-1934) are of great significance, and their ideas and discoveries have in large measure shaped the modern world and the way we think. The same is true in the fields of biology and medicine, where all the following have had their impact: Ambroise Paré (1509-1590), Pierre Fauchard (1678-1761), Le Chevalier Jean Baptiste de Lamarck (1744-1829), Baron Georges Cuvier (1769-1832), Marie Francois Bichat (1771-1802), Francois Magendie (1783-1855), Claude Bernard (1813-1878), Paul Bert (1833-1886) and Louis Pasteur (1822-1895). We will have much to say about many of these.

On the whole France is very good at preserving the historical aspects of her culture, but there have been some lapses, in particular the destruction that took place during their revolution (1789). A sorry chapter in human history, from which the historical associations of biology and medicine did not escape. Despite this, France is a wonderful country in which to see many aspects of biological and medical history. However, we feel compelled to point out that in order to do this effectively, it would be well if the visitor spoke a little French. It is important to realize that in France most museums and national monuments are closed on Tuesdays.

Roads in France are good, but it should be noted that almost all their "Autoroutes" are toll roads. All road directions we give are from Paris. The French National Railway (SNCF) is one of the finest in the world, with services to most parts of France. There are also many bus services.

Arbois (Jura)

Location - 390 kilometers southeast of Paris.

Train - From Paris (Gare de Lyon) to Dijon and Dôle, and then by taxi
   or bus to Arbois.

Road - Take the A6 (la Route du Sud) to the south and exit at
Beaune onto the N73 towards Dôle. Before enteringDôle turn
right onto the N5 towards Vaudrey and at Vaudrey branch onto
the N469 (also the D469) to Arbois.

Arbois, Jura, is a pleasant small town in Eastern France, not far
from the Swiss border, and it was here in 1827 that the parents of
Louis Pasteur (1822-1895)--see under Dôle and Paris--established
the family home, "Maison Familiale," which is now the Musée Louis
Pasteur, and virtually a French national shrine. Pasteur was brought
up here, and often returned here during his life.

Musée Louis Pasteur
83 rue de Courcelles
Arbois

Opening hours:
   April 15 - September 30. Daily 10.00 - 12.00 and 14.00 -
   17.30.
   November 1 - April 14. Daily 10.00 - 11.30 and 14.00 - 15.30.
   Closed Tuesdays.
   Small charge for admission.
   There is a guided tour (in French) every half hour.
   It should be noted that there is another Pasteur Museum in
   Dôle, only 30 kilometers away, and it is closed on Mondays.
   However, both should be visited while in the area.

With the possible exception of Napoleon Bonaparte, no
Frenchman is held in higher esteem than Louis Pasteur. He was
certainly one of the great geniuses of all time, and his contributions
to human welfare are unsurpasssed.

Louis Pasteur's father, Jean-Joseph Pasteur, was a native of
Besancon and a tanner by trade. He served with distinction in the
Grand Army of Napoleon, but after the latter's defeat at Waterloo in
1815, Jean-Joseph was discharged from the army, and settled in
Dôle in a house on the banks of the river Doubs where he could
pursue his tanner's trade. Here in 1822 Louis was born, but when
he was 5 his family moved to nearby Arbois, where the family home
was established, and where Louis was brought up. His father was an

avid believer in education, and took a personal interest in the schooling of his children to the point of going over their homework every evening and making sure they were progressing satisfactorily. Louis attended the local school in Arbois, but when he was 17 he went to the Royal College in nearby Besancon. At this time he displayed a remarkable talent for art (drawing, painting, etc.), and in fact he worked at this, from time to time, all his life. The art work he left is of high quality, and there is no doubt he could have been a professional artist had he so desired. Three years later in 1842 he received an arts degree from the Royal College, but it was not until he went to Paris the following year that he displayed an aptitude for science. In Paris he was admitted as a chemistry student to the prestigous École Normale Supérierure (see under Paris), then, as now, France's top college. Here he studied for 4 years, receiving his doctor's degree in 1847 with a thesis on crystallography. This terminated his formal education, and despite his immense contributions to biology and medicine, Pasteur was never a biologist or medical doctor. The research which he did for his doctoral thesis is known best to organic chemists, but his discoveries have had enormous impact far and wide. Basically what he accomplished was to show that two or more compounds of identical composition (he worked with tartaric acid) may display totally different properties, and he demonstrated that this was due to isomerism (i.e., the different arrangement of the atoms within the molecule). With this demonstration, stereochemistry (space chemistry) may be said to have begun, and the effects of this on chemistry, biology and medicine have been profound. Very few scientists have contributed really significant ideas and become famous while they were students. Sir Isaac Newton was one, so was Marie Curie, and Louis Pasteur was another.

In 1849, Pasteur was made a professor at the University of Strasbourg in eastern France. Here he continued his studies of crystallography, but perhaps more important to him personally was that here he met and married Marie Laurent, the daughter of the Rector of the university. She was his devoted wife until his death 46 years later, and she outlived him by 15 years. Madame Marie Pasteur, catered to her husband's needs, nursed him through illnesses, and brought up their children. She indeed is entitled to share in the triumphs of her husband, and the praise showered upon him.

His appointment at Strasbourg was followed in 1854 by a similar one at the University of Lille in Northern France, and here he started his work on the causes of fermentation which was to lead to his most important discoveries, both theoretical and practical. His appointment at Lille lasted only three years, for in 1857 he returned to his old college, the École Normale Supérieure, in Paris as Director of Scientific Studies. The research he started in Lille was on the phenomenon of fermentation, and it is important to realize that at that time virtually nothing was known as to how this took place. What Pasteur demonstrated was that it was the presence of minute but living organisms which caused fermentation, that different microorganisms caused different kinds of fermentation, and that some of these microorganisms grew in the absence of free oxygen. In time he also demonstrated that putrefaction was due to the presence of living organisms. The resulting applications of these discoveries were striking and rapid in coming, for not only did they open up a rational explanation of many biological phenomena, but also a means of controlling them. Thus it was possible to understand and control the fermentation of such things as beer and wine. In 1863 Pasteur was credited with saving the French wine industry, and no Frenchman ever performed a more patriotic act than that! This work also quickly led to the process we now call pasteurization, with all its beneficial consequences. The significance of his explanation of putrefaction was quickly understood by Joseph Lister in England (see under Glasgow and Edinburgh), and led to Lister's work in antiseptic surgery and therapy. Indeed Pasteur's work on microorganisms laid the foundation of the whole concept of the "germ theory of disease" with all its subsequent ramifications.

Pasteur's work on microorganisms also led him to a solution of a very important biological problem. In the middle of the 19th century, it was a hotly debated subject as to whether microbes could arise in the absence of other microbes. That is, could they come into existence by the so-called process of "spontaneous generation" from inanimate material? At that time it was not an easy problem to solve, but by rigorous design and clever experimentation he proved, in a remarkably short period of time, that spontaneous generation of microbes was a myth, and that all microbes were descended from other microbes. His conclusions have never been seriously challenged since.

By this time Pasteur was a very famous man, and his advice and services much in demand. In 1865, at the request of the French Government and the Emperor Napoleon III, he undertook to study the diseases of silkworms which at the time were devastating the important silk industry. These studies took nearly 5 years, which were interrupted for a long period in 1868 when Pasteur suffered a severe stroke which caused permanent paralysis of his left side--he was only 46. However, he recovered sufficiently to continue his work, and in due course not only solved the problems that were destroying the French silk industry, but at the same time realized the importance of experimental research on microorganisms in the study of biology and pathology. As a result of this realization he went on in the years that followed to attack the problems of many virulent diseases, including anthrax in sheep, chicken cholera and puerperal fever in humans. His successes were truly remarkable; one vaccine after the next was developed, including the attenuation of viruses which gave a means of controlling the deadly disease rabies, and subsequently many others.

As Pasteur grew older, the pace at which he worked inevitably declined. The French Government built in his honor, the Pasteur Institute in Paris, which contained private apartments for him and his wife. These are now a magnificent museum (see under Paris), but the research work of the institute, today greatly expanded, continues in the Pasteur tradition. However, the culminating tribute to Pasteur occurred on December 27, 1892, his seventieth birthday, when France honored him in a public ceremony held in the main theater of the Sorbonne. Almost every country in the world was represented, along with a distinguished international group of scientists. Pasteur was by this time in poor health, and his voice weak, but he bravely replied to the honors conferred upon him, and in so doing his life-long humanitarianism shone through. He said in part, "You have come from so far to give a proof of sympathy for France, you bring me the deepest joy a man can experience, who believes invincibly that science and peace will triumph over ignorance and war; that peoples will come to a common understanding, not to destroy but to build, and that the future will belong to those who will have done most for suffering humanity. . . ." -- Modern political leaders please note!

Louis Pasteur has often been described as the "ideal scientist," because not only were his scientific discoveries of unsurpassed importance and benefit, but all his life he was devoted to his country, his parents, his wife, his children and humanity at large. He was always in sympathy with those in trouble, and no one ever did more to help them.

The Maison Familiale in Arbois, together with the Maison Natale in Dôle, are owned and operated by the "Societé des Amis de la Maison Natale de Pasteur à Dôle." Each house has a curator ("le gardien"). There have been no essential alterations to the house in Arbois since Pasteur's day, and it is beautifully preserved. There is a ground floor, with two floors above, and the rooms are furnished with many objects associated with Pasteur and his family. His laboratory and study are located upstairs, and the former has a lot of the equipment he used for his experiments. In his study is a magnificent library, which contains all his works in their first editions, as well as much more. There are also many original documents, etc. associated with him. A visit to this museum, dedicated to preserving the memory of Louis Pasteur is a thrilling experience for one and all. The visitor to Arbois should also see the very lovely statue of Pasteur in the main square of the town, an easy walk from the Maison Familiale.

BEAUNE (Côte-d'Or)
Location - 310 kilometers southeast of Paris.
Train - From Paris (Gare de Lyon) to Dijon and Beaune.
Road - Take the A6 (la Route du Sud) to the south and exit at
     Beaune.

Beaune, Côte-d'Or, is primarily noted for two things. First it is the focal point of the Burgundy wine area, and secondly it has one of the oldest surviving hospitals in the world. It is a fascinating old town, with origins as far back as the 7th century. At first it was the capital of a separate Duchy, but in 1227 this was united to Burgundy, and became the seat of the Dukes of Burgundy. It is commonly referred to as "the wine capital of the world," and every year merchants come from the four corners of the earth to sample and bid for the wines of the area.

Hôtel Dieu
Place Carnot
Beaune

Opening hours:
     Daily, 9.00 - 11.15 and 14.00 - 17.00
     Small charge for admission.
     It may be seen by guided tour only. These tours are in
     French, but a printed English summary is available.

The Hôtel Dieu is one of the oldest surviving hospitals in the world. It was founded in 1443 by Nicholas Rolin, Chancellor of Burgundy, and his wife, Guigone de Salins, in response to the misery prevailing at the time. It was initially an endowed institution,

107

and possessed large areas of land. These lands, then as now, are largely vineyards producing some of the best wines in the world. Thus while the buildings are old, and the rules, customs and uniforms of the nursing sisters remain the same as when the hospital began caring for the sick, the vast wealth provided by its vineyards has enabled it to have the finest equipment and doctors in France.

By far the most impressive part of the hospital is "La Grand Salle," sometimes referred to as the Paupers Ward. It is in fact a combined hospital ward and chapel, so arranged that the patients confined to bed could take part in the religious services going on in the chapel; the overriding concern of the hospital being to save the soul as well as the body! This ward was used regularly until 1948, but is now simply maintained as a showpiece. It is 52 meters long, 16 meters high with a gothic vault, and a very impressive place. The beds down each side of the ward are "inbuilt," with double beds for two patients each! The chapel was damaged during the revolution, but was restored in the 19th century. It contains some magnificent stained glass windows. Other areas of immense interest include the Great Courtyard, the original kitchens and the dispensary. The latter restored in the 18th century, contains a remarkable collection of historical eating utensils used by the sick; jugs, mugs, bowls, etc., as well as drugs, medicines and medical instruments. Finally there is a special room housing the famous painting of " The Last Judgement" (painted about 1444) by Roger Van de Weyden, which was commissioned for the original hospital by its founder, Nicholas Rolin, and has been there ever since.

The Hôtel-Dieu is not only a very interesting architectural structure, but is of great interest in the history of medicine. Long may it live, and the vineyards that support it! The visitor to Beaune should also not miss the Wine Museum, formerly the Palace of the Dukes of Burgundy, and the Jules-Etienne Marey museum in the Hôtel de Ville. He was a pioneer photographer.

DOLE (Jura)
Location - 360 kilometers southeast of Paris.
Train - Paris (Gare de Lyon) to Dijon and Dôle.
Road - Take the A6 (la Route du Sud) to the south and exit at
        Beaune onto the N73 which leads directly into Dôle.

Dôle, Jura, has a history going back to Roman times. Later it was part of the Duchy of Burgundy until 1479 when it was captured and burnt by the army of Louis XI. Later still it fell into Austrian hands, but in 1674 was restored to France by Louis XIV. Perhaps more important than all this however, is that it was here, in 1822, that Louis Pasteur (see under Arbois and Paris) was born in his parents' house on the banks of a canal adjoining the river Doubs. The house is now a museum.

La Maison Natale de Pasteur
43 rue Louis Pasteur
Dôle

Opening hours:
> Tuesday - Sunday, 10.00 - 12.00 and 14.00 - 16.00.
> Closed Mondays.
> Small charge for admission.
> A tour (in French) is available.

La Maison Natale de Pasteur is just off the Quai Pasteur on the Tanners Canal, which is a short walk from the main street of the town. The house was built in 1750, and on December 27th, 1822, Louis Pasteur was born in one of the front rooms. It is preserved much as it would have been at that time. The other principle room in the house is, "La Salle A. Ventard." This was originally the tanner's drying room, but now a museum with a host of memorabilia very well displayed. The room is rich in documents and papers concerning Pasteur's chalk drawings and other art work, for which he had a remarkable talent. Visitors should also not miss the basement (Les Caves) of the house, with all the apparatus of the tanner's trade still preserved. Finally there is a very imposing statue of Pasteur in the park nearby.

It is hard to choose between this museum and the one in Arbois, both are truly gems, and both give an insight into the very simple background of Louis Pasteur, a simplicity to which he continued to adhere all his life.

MONTPELLIER (Herault)
Location - 750 kilometers south of Paris.
Train - Paris (Gare de Lyon) direct to Montpellier.
Road - Take the A6 (la Route du Sud) as far as Lyon. Then join the
  A7 to Orange and the A9 to Montpellier.

Montpellier is on the river Lez and situated only some 10 kilometers from the shores of the Mediterranean Sea. Originally it was a port, but over the centuries the land filled in, and the town of Sete is now Montpellier's port. Today Montpellier is a large, prosperous industrial town with a most interesting blend of the very old and the very new. The south of France is one of the most pleasant places on earth, something the Romans found out when they conquered the area (125-121 B.C.), and established a large province connecting Italy and Spain, which they called "Provence," a name which still survives. Montpellier was one of the chief Roman towns in the province, and has played a prominent role ever since. The Roman rule of the area lasted until the end of the 4th century A.D., and although then overthrown by Germanic hordes with terrible destruction, Roman culture nevertheless left its indelible mark which is still present today. For the next four centuries the area saw one conquest after the next, until Charlemagne (768-814) restored the Roman order. From this time until the present the area of Provence has prospered or suffered along with the rest of France. However, so far as Montpellier is concerned there is one period of great importance and that is the Wars of Religion, with Protestants against Roman Catholics, from 1520-1540. The French themselves describe this period as "the most ghastly in their history," and Montpellier, being a center of Protestantism, suffered badly. However, the scars of this devastation have largely healed, and today Montpellier is a blend of streets with their origins in the middle ages, the elegant 19th century Place de la Comédie (the town center) and ultra modern areas. But above all there is the superb old Medical School and the nearby Botanic Garden.

Le Faculté de Médecine
Rue de l'École de Médecine
(Off the Boulevard Henri IV)
Montpellier

Opening hours:
>Normal business hours.
>No charge for admission.

The Faculty of Medicine of the University of Montpellier is the oldest surviving medical school in the western world, and was for centuries one of the world leaders. Today it is still one of the foremost in France. One may walk through the public hallways and theaters, but permission from the Dean's office is required to see the restricted rooms and libraries. However, this can be obtained by really interested persons. The main building adjoins the cathedral, which indicates the religious origins of the school, and both can be seen at the same time.

The Faculty of Medicine, and with it the University of Montpellier, was founded on the 17th of August, 1221 by Cardinal Conrad, a papal legate from Pope Urban V, who was at that time the Pope at Avignon. Thus it has been in continuous existence for over 700 years. However, there is every evidence that medicine was studied in Montpellier long before 1221. This was in the rabbinic schools going back to the 11th century, and the names of some of the professors in these schools are actually preserved and are considered the forerunners of the faculty of medicine.

The building housing the present medical school was originally a monastery, and much of its 13th century walls survive intact. During the religious wars of the 16th century some of this building was destroyed, but in the following two centuries was rebuilt on the same foundations. The great anatomy theater was added in the 19th century. The basement (Salle Lapidaire or Salle Capitulaire) is an original room dating from the 13th century monastery, and the modern electron microscope rests on a 13th century wall!

In a special room of the library are housed an incredible collection of documents concerning the history of the university over its 700 years of existence. One of these dates from 1331, and comes from Philippe VI de Valois, who was the first king of France after Montpellier became part of France; in it he confirms the privileges of the university.

In the central entrance hallway, with its beautiful 18th century staircase, are a collection of busts of the great doctors going back to Hippocrates (460-357 B.C.), and also plaques showing the names of virtually all the professors of the medical school from the rabbinic period of the 11th century to the present day.

As the medical school has been in continuous existence for so long one might expect a superb historical library, and indeed this is the case. The office of the Dean is virtually an adjunct to the library, with huge circular stacks containing priceless old books. There are also two magnificent conference rooms (Salle des Actes), one for faculty, and one where graduates receive their degrees. The latter contains portraits of all their famous graduates going back to 1239, and include Francois Rabelais (1490-1553), who received his medical training there in 1537. The original matriculation entry with his signature is actually preserved in the library. It is perhaps significant that unlike many modern medical schools, graduates from Montpellier are still required to take the Hippocratic oath.

It is of great interest that right down to the time of the revolution, virtually all faculty were professors of anatomy in the winter and professors of botany in the summer! One of these, Pierre Richer de Belleval was the founder of the botanic garden and it has a close association with the medical school, both historically and physically.

Le Jardin des Plantes
Boulevard Henri IV
Montpellier

Opening hours:
> Monday - Friday, 8.00 - 12.00 and 14.00 - 18.00
> Saturdays, 8.00 - 12.00. Closed Sundays.
> No charge for admission.

The Botanic Garden of Montpellier is one of the oldest in the world, and in Europe is perhaps exceeded in age only by those at Padua (see under Padua, Italy) and Leipzig, East Germany.

Medical schools have always had medicinal herb gardens attached to them, and the evidence is strong that these existed in Montpellier as far back as the origins of the medical school. Indeed, legend has it that Apollo had been wandering as an exile through the south of France, and was so charmed by the pure air, courteous citizens, and abundance of plants at Montpellier, that he decided to found a medical school and herb garden there. However, the present gardens were founded in 1593 as "Le Jardin du Roi" in an edict to the University of Montpellier by King Henri IV (1553-1610). At the same time Pierre Richer de Belleval (1558-1623) was appointed professor of anatomy and botany, and director of the garden, with royal patronage. Belleval was one of those rare individuals who went about his job with unparalleled zeal, placing the establishment of the garden above all else. He was always in trouble with both the administration and the students, and for the usual reasons! The administration complained that he did not attend committee meetings or other formal functions, and the students complained that he was never there. No, he was out botanizing, and if it hadn't been for him there would be no botanic garden. We can get some idea of the enthusiasm botanists, then as now, get from botanizing, by quoting a German botanist, Leonard Fuchs, who wrote in 1542:

> But there is no reason why I should dilate at greater
> length upon the pleasantness and delight of
> acquiring knowledge of plants, since there is no

one who does not know that there is nothing in this life pleasanter and more delightful than to wander over woods, mountains, plains, garlanded and adorned with flowerlets and plants of various sorts, and most elegant to boot, and to gaze intently upon them. But it increases that pleasure and delight not a little, if there be added an acquaintance with the virtues and powers of these same plants.

Fortunately, Belleval was more or less immune from the admonitions of administrators and students, for he had the personal patronage of the king. In the years that followed he traveled widely collecting plants, and under his directorship the garden flourished.

In the last decade of the 16th century, Montpellier was emerging from the terrible religious wars of the earlier part of the century. King Henri IV was more or less tolerant of Protestant Montpellier, and the university and town were thriving. But in the winter of 1621 - 1622 disaster struck. The new king, Louis XIII, was not as tolerant of Protestants as his predecessor, and decided to bring Montpellier to heel. This he did with a vengeance. His troops actually camped in Belleval's newly established botanic garden and used the buildings for fortifications. It was completely destroyed! When Louis XIII entered the city and peace was restored, Belleval started all over again, and for the remaining years of his life once more put the garden above all else. With ups and downs, the garden has more or less prospered since then, and is still one of the best in the world. One might hope that by now everyone had learned to respect this triumph of scientific botany and beauty, but the dangers of the past have unfortunately not disappeared. As recently as 1975, there was a motion put before the Montpellier City Council to turn the botanic garden into a parking lot!

Over the main gate to the garden, and below the king's arms are inscribed the words "Hic Argus Esto et Non Biareus"--Be all eyes, not all hands here!-- and lovers of plants will appreciate the sentiment. The garden specializes in research on tropical and subtropical plants, and because of the mild climate there is always a good deal in bloom, some of it very exotic. There are both old and new glasshouses, and very interestingly, a whole array of garden sculpture in the form of busts of famous botanists throughout the centuries. In the main administration building, there are extensive research laboratories, and a magnificent botanical library with holdings going back many centuries. The laboratories and library are not normally open to the public, but one may ask (preferably in French!) to see them.

In ending this section on Montpellier, we can only say that the historical fascination of the town and the pleasant climate are exceeded only by the excitement of their medical school and botanic garden.

PARIS

Paris, the capital of France, is a vast city divided almost equally into two halves by the river Seine, the northern half being referred to as the right bank, and the southern half as the left bank. Paris is the unquestioned center of all French life, social, cultural, political, economic and administrative, and the variety of things to see and do are rivalled only by London. Visitors should avail themselves of good guidebooks and maps, and learn as quickly as possible how to use the excellent public transportation, particularly the underground trains (the Metro), but buses and taxis as well. Parisians have a saying that there are three very good and very cheap things in Paris, bread, wine, and the Metro--make use of them! Nothing however, beats walking to know a city, and Paris is a great city in which to walk. From a scientific point of view, with medicine and biology no exception, Paris has long been the focal point in France and there are many very interesting things to see.

It is appropriate that we start out with a few words of explanation about the University of Paris. Its founding goes back to the 13th century, when Pope Innocent III authorized the incorporation of a group of scholars, and from the very beginning there were various colleges. With the exception of a short period following the revolution, when it was closed by direct order of Napoleon Bonaparte, the university has been in continuous existence ever since, albeit with many changes. Today the University of Paris is a huge complex of semi-autonomous branches scattered all over Paris and its suburbs, but by far the most famous of these is "The Sorbonne."

La Sorbonne
Place de la Sorbonne
Paris 5^e

Opening hours:
> Normal weekday hours.
> No charge for admission.

Metro - Luxembourg, but Odéon or Maubert-Mutualité will do equally
> well.

The Sorbonne is on the left bank just off the Boulevard Saint
Michel in the heart of the "student-latin quarter." It was founded in
1252 by Robert de Sorbon (1201-1274) who was chaplain to King
Louis IX (Saint Louis), and with the consent of the king. From its
foundation until the revolution, it was devoted entirely to theology,
and was perhaps the greatest center of religious study in Europe.
This came to an abrupt end with the revolution, when the Sorbonne
was closed and all its property confiscated. However, with the
reorganization of the University of Paris in 1808, the Sorbonne was
reopened and became the seat of three faculties, literature, science
and theology. The present main building, bounded by the Rue
Victor Cousin, Rue de la Sorbonne, Rue des Écoles, Rue Saint
Jacques and Rue Cujas dates from 1889. It is a remarkable building,
housing lecture halls, museums, laboratories, libraries, offices, an
astronomy tower, amphitheaters and a chapel. Here in the
nineteenth century many great French scientists worked, but today
the Sorbonne is entirely Arts and Letters. It is a great experience to
walk through this building with all its historical associations, but the
"pièce de résistance" is Le Grand Amphitheatre (entrance from Rue
des Écoles). It may be seen, by permission, if it is not in use.

This amphitheater is of much historical interest to scientists,
because it is here that many great ceremonial events have taken
place, including the public honoring of Louis Pasteur on the
occasion of his 70th birthday in 1892. The amphitheater is in the
grand French style. On the domes of the roof are murals of the
symbols (all female!) of learning: literature, science, University of
Paris, medicine and law. There are also life sized statues of Robert
de Sorbon, Descartes, Lavoisier, Rollin, Pascal, Richelieu and
others. Finally on the walls of the balcony outside the amphitheater
itself are huge murals depicting various events in the history of
learning. It is really a very impressive place.

Collège de France
11 Place Marcelin-Berthelot
(Off Rue des Écoles)
Paris 5^e

Opening hours:
 Normal weekday hours.
 No charge for admission.
Metro - Maubert-Mutualité

The Collège de France is the premier academic institution in France. In French academic circles there is a popular saying "first you win the Nobel prize, then you will be elected to the Collège de France!" The college derives from the 17th century Royal College of France, but was founded in its present form in 1732 by Louis XV, and took its present name at the time of the revolution.

The function of the Collège de France is to supply a base for France's top scholars in all academic fields, allowing them the security and freedom to develop a new area of knowledge. The college gives no instruction, and grants no degrees. About the only requirement imposed on its members is that they give a few public lectures a year, and anyone may attend these. Its critics complain that the members become narrow and entrenched, but nevertheless there have been some brilliant scholars who have been members of the Collège de France, including the Egyptologist Jean Champollion (1790-1832), the zoologist Georges Cuvier (1769-1832), the chemist Frédéric Joliot-Curie (1900-1958), the physicist André Ampère (1775-1836), the poet Paul Valery (1871-1945), and most important for us, the physiologist Claude Bernard (1813-1878).

Outside the entrance to the Collège de France is a life-sized statue of Claude Bernard, whose life and work we describe under St. Julien-en-Beaujolais. Unfortunately in its prominent position it is subject to almost continuous vandalism! Nothing remains today of the laboratories in which Claude Bernard performed his brilliant work, however on the outside of the wing where he worked (on the Rue des Écoles) is a plaque commemorating his distinguished achievements there.

One may enter the Collège de France, by asking the permission of the concierge. However, visitors should remember that it is an active, working institution. Of particular interest is that in the director's office is a fine collection of instruments, formerly

116

belonging to Claude Bernard, as well as his death mask. These may be seen, by permission, if the director is not disturbed in so doing. In the Collège de France there are also busts, paintings, etc., of Claude Bernard and some of their other distinguished members.

Finally at 40 Rue des Écoles, directly opposite the Collège de France is the "Claude Bernard House." This is now a private residence, but there is a plaque on the wall indicating that Claude Bernard lived there for many years and also died there on February 10th, 1878.

Bibliothèque Saint Geneviève
10 Place du Panthéon
Paris 5^e

Opening hours:
    Normal weekday hours.
    No charge for admission.
Metro - Luxembourg, but Cardinal Lemoine will do equally well.

This is the main library of the Sorbonne, and is only a short walk from the latter. Permission is normally granted to see the main reading room, and it is not difficult to obtain a temporary permit to use the library, which contains many medical books of great historic interest.

The origins of the library go back to various religious orders and the founding of the Sorbonne in the 13th century. Until the revolution its holdings were mainly theology, but with the revolution all its holdings were nationalized. The University of Paris was completely reorganized, the scope of the library much enlarged and it now includes the natural sciences.

The present building dates from the middle of the 19th century, and many separate libraries were brought together there. Today it is one of the major libraries of France, with priceless collections going back five centuries. The building itself is an impressive structure. The main reading room is a classic piece of mid-19th century architecture and we recommend a visit to all those interested in academic history. Of interest also in the Place du Panthéon is the Panthéon, a national shrine, where many of France's great men are buried.

Musée de l'Histoire de la Médecine
Faculté de Médecine
Université de Paris
12 Rue de l'École de Médecine
Paris 6^e

Opening hours:
    Wednesday and Friday only, 14.00 - 18.00
    No charge for admission.
Metro-Odéon.

This is one of several medical schools within the University of Paris. It is situated just off the Boulevard St. Germain, close to where it crosses the Boulevard St. Michel. It is a huge complex, but from our point of view what is important about it is that on the second and third floors of the main building is a superb historical medical museum. Its name is Musée de l'Histoire de la Médecine, and the "conservateur" is Madame Jacqueline Sonolet (1981). She is also conservateur (curator) of the Musée Claude Bernard in St. Julien-en-Beaujolais (see elsewhere), and is obviously a master of the art. Madame Sonolet prefers to speak French, but in fact she speaks perfect English as well, and will always help out in the latter!

This is a very rich and well organized museum, with displays going back as far as Graeco-Roman times, but with heavy emphasis on the development of French medicine. It has a magnificent collection of prints and drawings going back centuries, and these are of extreme interest historically. There are also artifacts of all kinds. Although the museum is located in an old building, and crowded for space, it is not a static museum. One is brought right up to date with displays of modern instruments for microsurgery, and there are always new displays being arranged.

École Normale Supérieure
45 Rue D'Ulm
Paris 5^e

Opening hours:
    Normal business hours.
    No charge for admission.
Metro - Port-Royal, but Censier-Daubenton will do equally well.

The École Normale Supérieure is located in the heart of the latin-student quarter, not far from the Sorbonne. Today this is the top educational institution in France and from an academic standpoint very elite. Only 55 students, carefully chosen from all over France, are admitted each year, and for 4 years they receive intensive training to get their degrees. The institution also awards doctorate degrees, and there are extensive facilities for research particularly in the sciences. From an historical point of view, of great interest is that Louis Pasteur (see under Arbois and Dôle) was the Director here from 1857-1867, and here also he performed some of his classic experiments.

This educational institution was founded in 1794 by "The Convention" at the time of the revolution. Its initial function was to train teachers for French schools, but it has gradually evolved into its present elite status. It has stood on its present site since 1847, though the buildings have been vastly expanded over the years.

The building of historical interest is at 45 Rue D'Ulm, and one enters through iron gates, behind which is a portico and the office of the concierge, and beyond this is a large courtyard in the form of a handsome garden. On the four walls surrounding the courtyard are busts of many famous Frenchmen, including Ampére, Lavoisier, Juy-Lussac, Cuvier, Descartes, Moliére, Racine, LaFontaine, Voltaire, etc.--all very impressive, and even more so when it is realized that Louis Pasteur must have spent many hours in these same surroundings contemplating his next experiments.

However, "the gem" from a biologist's point of view is a small building just inside and to the right of the main gates. On the outside is a plaque which reads as follows:

Le Laboratoire de Pasteur
installe dans un grenier en 1857
fut etabli dans ce pavillon en 1860
et agrandi de batiments voisins
de 1862 - 1869.

(The laboratory of Pasteur installed in a granary in 1857,
was established in this pavilion in 1860, and enlarged by
adding the adjoining building from 1862 - 1869.)

This in fact is where Pasteur performed some of his classic experiments. The building is now used as an infirmary for the school, and the Matron lives there. However with special permission, and if the Matron is not too busy, she will take you up to the second floor (1^e etage) and show you the little attic cupboard (so small he had to work on his knees!) which Pasteur used as a culture room for his flasks. It was here that he did the experiments to disprove the "spontaneous generation of life." There is a plaque ouside the room commemorating the event, and the room is now used to store children's toys. Pasteur would have been happy about this. It gives one a great sense of respect, even humility to see the simple place where this great man worked and transformed so many aspects of our lives.

École Supérieure de Physique et de Chimie Industrielles de la Ville de Paris
10 Rue Vanquelin

Paris 5^e

Opening hours:
    Normal business hours.
    No charge for admission.
Metro - Censier-Daubenton, but Port-Royal or Place Monge will do
    equally well.

      This educational institution is situated right next to the École Normale Supérieure. In is not of direct medical or biological importance, but rather of physics and chemistry, for it was here in 1898 that Pierre and Marie Curie discovered the element radium and coined the word "radioactivity." There are a few things here which survive from this great and far-reaching event, and because of its importance to medicine and indeed all biology, we want to say a few words about this institution and the husband and wife who made such a momentous discovery here.

      Marie Curie (1867-1934) was born Marya Sklodowska in Warsaw, Poland, and from her earliest days she was recognized as a bright and enthusiastic student. Despite her parents' genuine concern for education, she received a very mediocre formal education, but was an avid reader and was largely self educated. Because of poverty within her family, and in order to educate her brothers and sisters, she went to work as a governess and remained in this capacity for some years. In 1891 at the age of 24, she left Poland and traveled to Paris. Then, as now (!) Poland was under the domination of Russia, and to Marie, France was the land of liberty and opportunity. Her dreams were, in this case to be fulfilled. Upon arriving in Paris, she immediately resumed her education, and in 1893 received a degree in physics and mathematics from the

University of Paris, ranking first in her class. The following year, while looking for a doctoral problem, she met Pierre Curie (1859-1906) at the École de Physique et Chimie where he was a professor, and went to work under him. They were married in 1895.

In the last decade of the 19th century, events were moving quickly in physics. In 1896, Henri Becquerel (1852-1908)--see under Musée National d'Historie Naturelle, Paris--had discovered and published his observations on the radioactivity of uranium, and these rays subsequently became known as Becquerel Rays. In 1898, just 3 years after Marie went to work in Pierre's laboratory, she and Pierre isolated, for the first time, the highly radioactive element radium. In 1903 Marie received her somewhat delayed doctorate degree, and the same year, she, her husband and Henri Becquerel were awarded the Nobel prize for their work. As a result of their research a new era in physics and chemistry was opened, which has had profound consequences for us all. With the discovery of radioactivity and radium in particular, Marie firmly believed that she and her coworkers had found at last the ever-elusive "cure for cancer." Unfortunately, this did not prove to be the case, though of course it has been of great value in controlling some aspects of the disease.

Up until this time, life had been hard for the Curies, but they were a happy couple and enjoyed a simple life. In 1906 Marie was made a professor at the Sorbonne, the first woman to hold such a post, but in the same year disaster struck with the death of her husband, who was run over by a dray in the streets of Paris. Marie never really recovered from this, and her only compensation was to immerse herself in work. Her brilliant mind continued to unravel the mysteries of radioactivity and in 1911 she was awarded the Nobel prize for the second time. Honors and fame poured in for her, but she continued a quiet life and increasingly devoted her skills to medical applications of radiology. The harmful effects of radioactivity (unknown then), to which she was continuously exposed, took their toll on her health and she gradually became unable to work effectively. She died in a sanatorium in 1934. Marie was a remarkable human being, and her name will live on, perpetuated in "the curie" now the physical unit of radioactivity. One short epilogue, Marie and Pierre's daughter, Irène, who became the wife of the French physicist Frédéric Joliot, also won the Nobel prize in 1935, a year after her mother's death.

Unfortunately the laboratory of Pierre and Marie Curie at the École Supérieure de Physique et de Chimie does not survive, but the portico to the original institution does, and outside there is a plaque commemorating their discovery. However, in a hallway outside the director's office (which can be seen by permission) is a case containing some of the Curies' original apparatus and instruments. Also some of their own notes and published articles. To see these is well worth the effort, but it is a pity that more is not preserved of this momentous discovery.

Musée National d'Histoire Naturelle-Jardin des Plantes
Place Valhubert/Rue Cuvier/Rue Geoffroy St. Hilaire

Paris 5^e

Opening hours:
>   Daily, 8.00 - 10 minutes before sunset.
>   Various buildings are open at different times, but all are closed on Tuesdays.
>   No charge for admission.

Metro - Austerlitz (which is the same as Gare d'Orléans). This is for the main entrance on Place Valhubert, but there are other entrances.

This massive institution is the principle Natural History complex of France, and it occupies a whole block facing onto the Seine along the Quai Saint Bernard and opposite the Pont d'Austerlitz. It was founded in 1635 as "Le Jardin Royal," and initially was the Royal Medicinal Herb Garden of Louis XIII. However, under Louis XIV (1638-1715) it underwent great expansion both in size and functions. Botanists were sent out all over the world to collect plants and bring them back to Le Jardin Royal. Animals were also included in the collections, and geological specimens as well. In this way, a thriving institution of scientific botany, zoology and geology was established, and has more or less prospered ever since. With the coming of the revolution, Le Jardin Royal received a new charter and was renamed Le Musée National d'Histoire Naturelle. Today its operation comes under the ultimate authority of the Minister of Education, and its functions are collecting, research and education, not just in natural history, but in all the natural sciences. Many great scientists have worked here at one time or another.

In English-speaking countries we tend to emphasize the achievements of our own compatriots, and forget that the French (and other peoples) had their counterparts who made enormous contributions to human knowledge. For example Le Comte George

Louis de Buffon (1708-1788), Le Chevalier Jean Baptiste de Lamarck (1744-1829), Georges Cuvier (1769-1832) and Henri Becquerel (1852-1908)-see elsewhere-all worked at Le Musée National d'Histoire Naturelle, and they played an enormous role in the development of biology. Thus a few words about them are in order.

Jean Baptiste Lamarck is probably the most maligned scientist in the English-speaking world. Professors of genetics commonly mention his name in an introductory lecture and then proceed to trample him underfoot and tell their students "never let me hear you mention his name." However, that is a very short-sighted and totally false view of Lamarck, who in our opinion was second only to Darwin! He was born in the small village of Bazentine-le-Petit in northeastern France. His family is described as minor nobility without wealth, and the latter certainly characterizes Lamarck's life, for he was always poor, and at his death there was not even enough money to pay for his funeral. As a boy he studied under the Jesuits in Amiens, but this did not last long, and at the early age of 15 he joined the French Army. He saw active service, traveled widely, and most important of all, for his future career, began botanizing. After some 10 years in the army he was forced by ill health to leave, and found his way to Paris where he studied medicine. As a result of his botanical knowledge he was soon elected to the Academy of Sciences, and in 1788 was also appointed to the staff of Le Jardin du Roi. Lamarck took an active role in the reorganization of this garden at the time of the revolution, and when it subsequently became Le Musée National d'Histoire Naturelle, he remained with it for the rest of his life and there he did all his important work. Lamarck's private life can only be described as tragic. He married three times, each wife dying early in life, and he could never properly support his many children. Tragically also, he went completely blind for the last 10 years of his life.

Lamarck's scientific works covered a wide range of knowledge of chemistry, meteorology and geology. Most important was the fact that he also tried to grasp the underlying principles of each discipline and did not concern himself with minor details. His fame rests on his magnificent botanical and zoological works, and above all on his clearly stated theory of evolution. His Flore Francaise, published in 3 volumes in 1779, not only described accurately all the then known French plants, but introduced a system of natural classification much better than that of Carl Linnaeus, and this classification probably set his mind to work on his eventual theory of evolution. He did much the same thing with invertebrate animals, and his findings were published in two major works, Système des animaux sans vertèbres (1801) and his seven volume work, Histoire naturelle des animaux sans vertèbres (1815-1822). It was in these that he first discussed his theory of evolution, and also in Philosophe Zoologique (1809). Lamarck's ideas on evolution are complex and scattered throughout his books, but there can be no doubt that he came to believe in the gradual development through time of animals and plants evolving from pre-existing ones. The great problem in his mind was "how". He proposed the theory that the environment acted on living things in such a way as to change their characteristics making them more adaptable to that environment, and that these newly developed characteristics were then inherited by the offspring. This theory of Lamarck's, commonly referred to as "the inheritance of acquired characteristics," has subsequently proven to be incorrect, and a much better explanation was to be given by Charles Darwin. As a result Lamarck's reputation has suffered badly, and he has even been ridiculed in scientific circles. This, in our opinion, is most unjust. His contributions to general biological thought and knowledge were enormous, and he supplied the first clearly stated theory of evolution. He died unheralded in Paris in 1829, two years before Charles Darwin was to sail on the voyage of the Beagle. However, today he is not forgotten in French scientific circles, and just inside the main entrance of the museum, and dominating the whole scene is a very lovely statue of Jean Baptiste Lamarck, and this "sets the tone" for the whole institution. Below Lamarck's name on the statue are inscribed the following words:

Au
Fondateur de la Doctrine
de l'Evolution
Subscription Universelle
1908

Although the senior author of this book is himself a Darwinian scholar, we nevertheless agree with the French. Lamarck was the founder of the doctrine of evolution. It is not generally known that he also played a major role in the formulation and elucidation of the cell theory.

Henri Becquerel was born in 1852 within the grounds of Le Musée National d'Histoire Naturelle, where his father was a professor of physics, as was his grandfather also. Thus he was born and brought up in a scientific environment. He had the best schooling Paris could offer, receiving an engineering degree in 1877. He subsequently held high rank in the French civil service, as well as research and teaching appointments at various scientific schools and at Le Musée National d'Histoire Naturelle.

Becquerel's life was by no means entirely devoted to research in physics, but in 1896 he made the remarkable discovery of ionizing radiation from the element uranium, and thus opened the way for the modern science of nuclear physics. He subsequently worked closely with Pierre and Marie Curie (see elsewhere) with whom he shared the Nobel prize in 1903. The importance of Becquerel's discovery of radioactivity (a word coined by Marie Curie), can hardly be overestimated for its influence not only on physics, but also on biology and medicine, and it was here at Le Musée where the discovery took place. He died in Brittany in 1908. In a building bordering the Rue Cuvier, Becquerel had his laboratory and outside this is a plaque with the inscription:

Dans le Laboratoire
de Physique Appliquer du Muséum
Henri Becquerel
a Decouvert la Radioactivite
le 1er Mars 1896

For better or worse the world has never been the same since.

George Louis Buffon was born in Montbard (Burgundy) in 1707. He was the son of a first generation noble family, and when George was 10 the family moved to nearby Dijon. Here he studied at the College of the Jesuits, and demonstrated a real ability in mathematics. He also studied law and botany and at the age of 23 he traveled widely in Western Europe. Returning from his journeys he settled in Paris, and soon established himself in political and scientific circles, and devoted his main efforts to biology and natural history, but he also studied chemistry and geology. So successful was he that in 1739, at the early age of 32, he was appointed director of Le Jardin Royal or Le Jardin du Roi, as it was also called, and was associated with this for the rest of his life. Under Buffon's directorship Le Jardin Royal was transformed from what was basically a herb and exotic plant garden, into one of the foremost scientific institutions in the world. Buffon wrote many articles and books, but he is remembered mainly for his Histoire Naturelle, published in 36 volumes between 1749-1767. The importance of this work can hardly be overestimated, for in it and his other ancillary works, he investigated and discussed almost every aspect of natural science. Botany, zoology, geology, paleontology, the classification of animals and plants, the origin and age of the earth all came under his scrutiny. Also of prime importance was his insistence that science must be separated from theology, and that natural mechanisms are the only valid ones in science. Thus he fully understood the origins and nature of fossils, rejected the then accepted theory of catastrophes, including the Biblical flood as a means of explaining the earth's history, and revised the ideas of the age of the earth making it much older than the Biblical account. He also discussed the origin of life on earth, and had remarkably modern ideas on this subject. He certainly cannot be described as an evolutionist, though he did discuss the inheritance of acquired characteristics. However, we may summarize his work by saying that he provided the basic knowledge which was to be transformed by Lamarck, Cuvier and Darwin into our modern concepts of biology and geology. Buffon was a remarkably able and productive man, to whom the development of science owes a great deal. He died in Paris in 1788.

Georges Cuvier was born in 1769 in Montbeliard, Doubs. At that time the area was subject to the rule of the Duke of Wurttemberg. His family was poor, but not destitute, and Georges was considered a gifted child with an astonishing ability to learn. He showed a great interest in natural history from the earliest age.

When he was 15 years old he went to the Caroline University in Stuttgart, where he distinguished himself and made many friends. However, when he graduated in 1788, he could not find any appropriate job, and ended up as a tutor to a wealthy family near Caen in Normandy. This lasted for 6 years, during which he enormously increased his general knowledge, and particularly that of natural history. At this time he established his lifelong pattern of careful observation, but avoided theorizing. In 1795 he came to Paris, was soon on the staff of Le Musée d'Histoire Naturelle, and at the turn of the century was also made a professor at Le Collège de France. He had a house in the Jardin des Plantes and lived there until his death.

Cuvier's life is bound up with administration and politics, as well as natural history, but it is in the latter field that his fame rests. Under his direction, the collections of the museum were vastly increased, and it became then the foremost natural history museum in the world. Over the years he studied and wrote extensively in

126

zoology, comparative anatomy and paleontology. In his day he probably knew more than anyone else about fossil animals, and he is still considered a giant of the field. Despite this he never abandoned his faith in the Bible and creationist view of life. This brought him into sharp conflict with Lamarck and others such as Geoffroy Saint-Hilaire, whom he positively ridiculed. There is some reason to believe that Cuvier's beliefs in this regard were greatly influenced by political realities. Others infer that he clung closely to religion as a compensation for the tragedies he suffered. In 1804, relatively late in life he married a widow, Madam Davaucelle, by whom he had four children, but they all died before him! Be this as it may, Cuvier's scientific contributions were enormous, and he also served the very useful purpose of stimulating evolutionary thoughts by his astute and intelligent criticisms of them. He died in Paris in 1832, greatly revered by his fellow countrymen.

There are many places of great historical interest within the grounds of the museum, but we just want to mention one more in particular, and it is the magnificent library, La Bibliothèque de Musée National d'Histoire Naturelle. It is located next to the zoological galleries bordering la Rue Geoffroy St. Hilaire. This is a modern building complex, and it houses one of the best biological science collections in the world, with priceless holdings going back centuries. Application to use the library may be made at the main desk, and it is not difficult to obtain. The stacks are not open to the public, but a professional librarian will bring anything to the reading room upon request. The card index is easy to use. We can mention also that as one enters the main lobby of the building, there are on either side, larger than life murals depicting with freshness and clarity the world's great naturalists and explorers, by the artist Raoul Dufy (1878-1953).

In conclusion, we will say that Le Musée National d'Histoire Naturelle is full of scientific history and a wonderful place to spend an hour, a day or a week!

Académie National des Sciences
Place de l'Institut
23 Quai de Conti
Paris 6^e

Opening hours:
    Normal business hours.
    No charge for admission.
Metro - Pont Neuf.

This is also known as the Institut de France, and is the senior scientific body of the country. It is the equivalent of the Royal Society in England, or the National Academy of Sciences in the United States. It is located on the left bank opposite Le Pont des Arts. The buildings in which L'Académie National des Sciences are housed are not generally open to the public, however, one may ask the permission of the concierge to look around or be shown around. As is somewhat typical of French institutions of its type, the buildings are spacious, elaborately decorated, and there are a quantity of busts and portraits of famous French scientists. An interesting scientific place steeped in history.

Académie de Médecine
16 Rue Bonaparte
Paris 6^e

Opening hours:
    Normal business hours.
    No charge for admission.
Metro - St. Germain des Prés.

This is the senior medical institute of France, with a long history. It is on the left bank, just around the corner from La Place de l'Institut. Once again this is not really open to the public, but permission to see around may be obtained from the concierge. It is a very impressive building. Of particular interest are the three main meeting rooms, La Grand Salle for general assemblies, La Petit Salle for conferences, and La Salle Bader in which there are busts of virtually all the great French doctors throughout history. There are many more busts and portraits in the lobbies and hallways.

However, by far the most valuable asset of L'Académie de Médecine is its superb and priceless medical library. The library is scattered throughout the whole building, but there is a central reception and reading area. Permission for qualified scholars to use the library is relatively easy to obtain (unusual in France). The librarian is very cooperative and will produce almost any medical book of historical significance upon request. We asked to see the first edition (1543) of Vesalius' Anatomy, and it was produced within minutes! It is a very lovely experience to see "the home" of French medicine.

Faculté de Médecine
Université de Paris
45 Rue Saints Peres
Paris 6^e

Opening hours:
> Tuesdays and Fridays only, 14.30 - 17.00.
> No charge for admission.
> Children are not admitted.
Metro - St. Germain des Prés.

This is one of several faculties of medicine of the University of Paris, but it is of special interest in that it has two superb medical museums, which are called Le Musée Orfila and Le Musée Rouviere. To see these one must be accompanied by an attendant, and permission to enter has to be obtained at the office on the 6e etage (7th floor). The museums themselves are on the 8e etage (9th floor). Some background of medical and biological knowledge is necessary to appreciate them.

Le Musée Orfila is primarily comparative anatomy, and a marvelous place to see the anatomical evolutionary development of animals. Le Musée Rouviere is devoted to human anatomy. The displays are extensive, beautifully dissected, and comprise whole cadavers, skeletons, skulls, muscles, internal organs, sense organs, etc. There are also casts of the brains of former professors! These two museums are of great interest and value to the biologically and medically oriented.

Musée Fauchard et Bibliothèque
École Dentaire de Paris
45 Rue de la Tour d'Auvergne
Paris 9^e

Opening hours:
    Monday - Thursday only, 9.30 - 12.00 and 14.30 - 17.00
    No charge for admission.
Metro - St. Georges.

This is one of two dental schools in the University of Paris, but this one is of particular interest for its superb dental museum and library. The museum and library are named after the great French dentist Pierre Fauchard (1678-1761), who is universally acclaimed as the "Father of Dentistry." Almost everyone has suffered from some problems of the teeth, but without the pioneer work of Pierre Fauchard the modern dentist would not have come into being, and thus all mankind owes him a debt of gratitude. Considering the importance of Pierre Fauchard in the history of dentristry, it is remarkable so little is known about his life. He was born in Brittany in 1678. We know nothing about his education, except that he indicates most of it was self education, and certainly he had no formal training in dentistry. He became the "leading dentist of Paris," and died there in 1761 at the age of 83.

In 1728 he published his major work in two volumes. Amazingly enough the original manuscript survives! The title of the work is long, but is important because it indicates the thoroughness and comprehensiveness of the book. In English translation it reads: "The Surgeon Dentist or Treatise on the Teeth: In which it is seen the means used to keep them clean and healthy, of beautifying them, of repairing their loss and remedies for their diseases and those of the gums and for accidents which may befall the other parts in their vicinity--with observations and reflections on several special cases. A work enhanced by forty-two illustrations." There can be no doubt that this is the first scientific work on dentistry, and from it the modern science derives. In the preface, Fauchard gives credit to his predecessors, but they are really insignificant compared to his own genius. The title of the work indicates its scope, but its novelties have become part and parcel of modern dentistry. For example, he was the first to use and describe metal bands for correcting irregularities of the teeth, and he also used antiseptic methods in filling teeth long before the germ theory of infection was put forth.

The illustrations of the instruments he developed and used, are not unlike those in a dentist's tray of today.

Pierre Fauchard's ideas and methods spread far and wide, and they were adopted particularly rapidly in the newer, less traditional societies like the United States. Indeed, the United States' pre-eminence in modern dentistry derives from Pierre Fauchard.

The Museum and Historical Library of the Dental School are under the care (1981) of Mlle. Ghislaine de la Riviere, who is very knowledgeable and cooperative. The library is priceless and holds virtually every major work in the history of dentistry. Some of its very special books are displayed under glass. Permission to use the library is granted only to qualified scholars. The main room of the museum is surrounded on all four walls by display cases devoted to the history of dentistry. Unfortunately the displays comprise only a fraction of their collection, which is mostly stored in crates due to lack of space. However, the displays are fascinating and comprise such things as comparative dental anatomy of extinct and living animals, and a prized possession of a case of early 19th century dental instruments made for the dentist of King Charles X. This huge set of instruments is decorated in "mother of pearl," and a real gem to see. There is of course much more, and this is a very special place for those concerned with the history of dentistry.

Bibliothèque National
58 Rue Richelieu
Paris 2^e

Opening hours:
> Daily, 9.00 - 18.00, but the times of opening of various departments vary considerably.
> No charge for admission, but special permission is required to use it.

Metro - Bourse.

This is the national library of France, comparable to the British Library in Britain or the Library of Congress in the United States.

La Bibliothèque National has a long and complicated history, which it is not pertinent to describe in detail here. Briefly its origins go back to the 14th century when it was founded by King Charles V in La Tour de Louvre. However, in the following century King

Charles VIII and Louis XIII moved it to Le Château d'Amboise in the valley of the Loire. This was one of many royal castles in the area, and the library remained there for over a century. However in the 16th century, it was moved back to Paris and has remained there ever since. In 1537 Francis I signed a copyright law, granting the National Library a "duty copy" of every book published in France.

Over the centuries it has grown enormously, and is now one of the major libraries of the world and the depository of many major scientific works, such as all the 138 notebooks and correspondence of Louis Pasteur.

The architecture of the library is truly beautiful, and one may ask permission to see La Grand Salle and other major rooms. In addition there are Les Galeries Mansart et Mazarine, where there are often special exhibits. One cannot fail to enjoy a visit to this great library.

Musée Pasteur
Institut Pasteur
25 Rue du Docteur Roux
(Off Boulevard Pasteur)
Paris 15^e

Opening hours:
> Monday - Friday, 9.30 - 12.00 and 14.00 - 17.00
> No Charge for admission.
> Guided tours are available in French only.
Metro - Pasteur.

The Pasteur Institute is now made up of many buildings devoted to biological research, but the original building with its museum, was constructed by the French government in honor of Pasteur during his lifetime (for a short biography of Pasteur see under Arbois). During its construction, there was an apartment built right into it as living quarters for Pasteur and his wife. Today this comprises the Pasteur museum, and in most of the rooms things have been left much as he and his wife would have known them.

From a scientist's point of view, perhaps the most interesting room is "La Salle de Souvenirs Scientifiques." Beautifully displayed here, are most of the brilliant experiments and achievements of Pasteur. In looking at these, it should be remembered that Pasteur was primarily a physicist and chemist, and applied this knowledge to biology. He was never a medical doctor, yet no one ever did more for medicine. Much of the equipment in these displays was originally used by Pasteur, and a lot of it was made with his own hands.

The rest of the museum comprises seven rooms, showing the private living quarters of Pasteur and his wife. All their original furniture is there, and many of the walls are adorned with the paintings of Pasteur himself, who was a skilled artist. Also in La Grand Salle à Manger (the dining room) there is a magnificent portrait of the Italian biologist, Lazzaro Spallanzani (1729-1799), whom Pasteur greatly admired.

In the basement of the institute is the room in which Pasteur and his wife are buried. This is open to the public upon request at the museum desk. At the time of his death (1895) there was much pressure to have him buried in the Panthéon along with other great Frenchmen, though his family wanted him buried in his home environment at Arbois or Dôle. However, his scientific friends and colleagues pressed to have him buried in the Institut Pasteur, and their wishes finally prevailed. The crypt containing the tomb is really very beautiful, and is decorated in mosaic tiles. On the walls is a summary of his life's work, and in translation it reads as follows:

1848 Molecular dissymmetry
1857 Fermentations
1862 Spontaneous generation
1863 Studies in wine
1865 Maladies of silkworms
1871 Studies on beer
1877 Studies of virulent maladies
1880 Attenuation of viruses-vaccines
1885 Prophylaxis of rabies

On the ceiling at the four corners are the words foi (faith), esperance (hope), charité (charity), science (science), and these well express the criteria by which Pasteur lived his life.

Finally in the Institut Pasteur is the very impressive main library, which Pasteur himself used. It is particularly nice to see here that many of Pasteur's collaborators, including Charles Chamberland (1851-1908) and Emile Roux (1853-1933), are not forgotten in the great achievements of their master.

All in all a visit to the Institut Pasteur is a very interesting educational and moving experience. All done in excellent taste, and superbly kept and managed.

Le Conservatoire National des Arts et Métiers
292 Rue Saint-Martin
Paris 3e

Opening hours:
>   Tuesday - Friday, 14.00 - 17.30
>   Saturdays, 9.00 - 16.30
>   Sundays, 14.00 - 17.30; closed Mondays.
>   No charge for admission.
Metro - Reaumur-Sebastopol.

This is France's National Museum of arts and technology. Its origins go back to the revolution in 1794, when it was founded by public order of "The Convention." It preserves and displays the historical development of the graphic arts, photography, electricity and electronics, industrial machines, physical instruments, astronomy, etc. It is not primarily concerned with biology, but in this regard it has a fine display of the apparatus and instruments belonging to Antoine Laurent Lavoisier (1743-1794). Although a chemist by profession, Lavoisier's contribution to biology cannot be overestimated, mainly from his discovery of the true nature of combustion, and his application of chemistry to biology. With the publication of his Traité Eléméntaire de Chimie in 1789, modern chemistry is said to have begun, and its influence on modern biology was not long delayed.

Included in the Lavoisier collection at the museum are his desk, balances, thermometers, calorimeters, etc. These alone are worth a visit, but there is much more to delight anyone interested in the history of science and technology.

Le Hôtel Dieu
Place du Parvis
Ile de la Cité
Paris 4e

Opening hours:
>   Normal business hours.
>   No charge for admission.
Metro-Le Cité.

The Hôtel Dieu is on the main island (Ile de la Cité) in the Seine river, and borders the same square (Place du Parvis) as Notre Dame Cathedral.

This is one of the oldest hospitals in Europe, having been founded in 660 by St. Landry, the Bishop of Paris. It has been destroyed and rebuilt many times since then, but the original site was just across the square where the statue of Charlemagne now stands. Today it is a modern and active hospital, but visitors are welcome to walk in the central courtyard, around the porticos, where there are large murals and photographs depicting the development and important events in the history of medicine and the hospital.

Cimetière du Père-Lachaise
Boulevard Ménilmontant
Paris 20^e

Opening hours:
>Daily, 9.00 - dusk.
>No charge for admission.
>Le Bureau de Conservation near the entrance, will locate the grave of anyone buried there.

Metro - Père-Lachaise.

It is fitting that this section on Paris should end with its famous cemetery Père-Lachaise. It is a beautiful cemetery and a pleasure to walk in, but what is so remarkable about it is the number of very famous people, including many scientists, who are buried there. A few of these are Rossini, Colette, Heloise and Abèlard, Frédéric Chopin, Champollion, Daumier, Moliére, Gay-Lussac, Beaumarchais, Marshal Ney, Sarah Bernhardt, Balzac, Delacroix, Bizet, Proust, Isidora Duncan, Oscar Wilde, and to the great interest of all physiologists and medical doctors, Claude Bernard (see under St. Julien-en-Beaujolais). The location of Claude Bernard's grave is Division 20, Line 8, Number 18, but even then it takes a little effort to find it. However, it is worth it just to see the resting place of this great man to whom we owe so much. It is a simple grave, and on the tombstone are carved the following words--in translation:

Claude Bernard
Member of the Institute
Academy of Sciences and French Academy
Professor at the College of France

and at the Natural History Museum
Honorary Professor at the Faculty of Sciences
Member of the Academy of Medicine
President of the Society of Biology
Former Senator
Commander of the Legion of Honor
Born at St. Julien (Rhône) 11th July 1813
Died at Paris 10th February 1878.

St. JULIEN-EN-BEAUJOLAIS (Rhône)

Location - 440 kilometers south of Paris.

Train - Paris (Gare de Lyon) to Lyon, and then by bus or taxi to St. Julien-en-Beaujolais.

Road - Take the A6 (la Route du Sud) towards Lyon. About 30 kilometers north of Lyon turn off to Villefranche-sur-Saone. Then take the D35 (la Route du Beaujolais) to the west and to Saint Julien sur/sous Montmelas--also called St. Julien-en-Beaujolais.

St. Julien-en-Beaujolais, Rhône, is a small village in the heart of the Beaujolais wine area, but is also noted for the fact that it was here in 1813 that Claude Bernard (see also under Paris) was born. Today there is a very fine museum here of recent origin, kept in his honor.

Le Musée Claude Bernard

Route D76
St. Julien-en-Beaujolais

Opening hours:
Tuesday - Sunday, 10.00 - 12.00 and 14.00 - 18.00.
Closed Mondays and for the month of March.
Small charge for admission.

Claude Bernard (1813-1878), is universally regarded as the founder of experimental physiology, a method of research which, since his time has given rise to untold insights and discoveries about living phenomena. He was the son of poor vineyard workers in Beaujolais, and received a very sparse education, with no science at all, but he loved all natural things, and had an inquiring mind. As a young man he worked under an apothecary, but soon turned his talents to the theater, writing comedies. These were successful enough, that he was soon in Paris, but there he was dissuaded from pursuing a literary career. Instead he studied medicine, and for a time interned at the Hôtel Dieu (see under Paris) under the most famous physician of the day, Francois Magendie. In 1841, at the age of 28, he followed Magendie to the Collège de France (see under Paris). Magendie was an experimenter, and from him Claude Bernard learned the concepts and techniques which he was to put to such great use.

In the meantime he married in haste, and it is said for money, the daughter of a Parisian physician, Fanny Martin. This unfortunately turned out to be a classic case of the lines by William Congreve (1670-1729) "Marry'd in haste, we repent at leisure," for he had a miserable conjugal life.

In 1852, Magendie retired, and Claude Bernard succeeded to his chair at the Collège de France, and for the next twenty years he made one brilliant discovery after the next, making his name a legend. It has often been said, that had Nobel prizes been awarded in Claude Bernard's day, that he would have won several. His accomplishments and discoveries include:

1. The digestive function of the pancreas.
2. The glycogenic and other functions of the liver.
3. The discovery of the vasoconstrictor and vasodilator nerves and their mechanisms of functioning.
4. The concept of the "milieu intérieur" (internal environment), now referred to as homeostasis.
5. His studies on the action of drugs, particularly curare, and their application to medicine.
6. The functions of bile.
7. Nerve innovation of the vocal chords, and the functions of the cranial nervers.
8. The inhibitory action of the vagus nerve on the heart.
9. The production of experimental diabetes. In fact, he only just missed discovering the cause of diabetes.

However, more than all this was his establishment of experimental physiology as a valuable tool to the understanding of how living things work. As he himself put it "La source unique de nos connaissances est l'experimentation" (Experimentation is a unique source of knowledge). His great work "Introduction à l'Étude de la Médecine Expérimentale" published in 1865 is one of the milestones in physiology and medicine.

Throughout his life, whenever his duties in Paris would permit, Claude Bernard returned to his home in St. Julien-en-Beaujolais. In due course he bought the manor house and vineyards where his parents had worked, and he was himself an avid viticulturist. His later years were plagued by illness, but were happier in the sense that he was separated from his wife. He died in Paris in 1878 and was accorded a state funeral, hitherto reserved for famous politicians and generals.

Le Musée Claude Bernard (owned and operated by La Fondation Merieux de Lyon) is in the house which he bought and so often returned to. It is located just in front of the house where he was born "La Maison Natale", and there is a plaque on this commemorating the event. All the rooms on the ground and 1e etage (second floor) of the museum are devoted to the life history and achievements of Claude Bernard. It consists of various exhibits of his famous laboratory experiments, his instruments, kymographs, balances, documents, etc., his M.D. thesis, and all his published works in their original editions. Much of the furniture in the rooms is original. There are also many portraits, busts and photographs and events from his private life. Copies of his theatrical works, such as "La Rose du Rhône" and others are there, also an autographed copy of Emile Zola's famous novel "Le Docteur Pascal," which was based on the life of Claude Bernard. There are many other things to see there, and in our opinion it is "a gem."

The museum house, built of soft yellow stone, is set in beautiful countryside, and surrounded by the same vineyards which Claude Bernard cultivated.

This is a pleasant place to close our dialogue on the biological and medical history of France. However, before leaving the Beaujolais area, we would like to suggest that you drive around it on "La Route des Beaujolais Villages", and perhaps end up with a meal at Le Restaurant du Beaujolais (closed Tuesdays) in the little village of Blaceret, just 5 kilometers north of St. Julien-en-Beaujolais. It is a Guide Michelin one star restaurant, and a fitting place to celebrate the life of Claude Bernard and the blessings we owe to him.

Chapter 3

FEDERAL REPUBLIC OF GERMANY

(WEST GERMANY)

Like France and Britain, Germany has traditionally been one of the top ranking countries in the world in the advance of biological and medical knowledge. In the 19th century, Germany took second place to none in science, but with the coming of World War I and particularly the Nazi regime of the nineteen thirties, followed by World War II, Germany's scientific position declined, and is only now coming back into its own. Furthermore from our particular point of view here, the destruction occasioned by World War II was so great that much of Germany's visible and tangible scientific heritage has gone forever. Nevertheless, some things survive, which we will describe, and we will also explain other important aspects of which there is virtually no surviving record. Germany is politically divided into West and East, a division stemming from the end of World War II. West Germany is a very beautiful country, and has excellent roads, their "Autobahns" being the originators of our freeways. However, there are often much more pleasant routes than the Autobahns. All road directions we give are from Bonn, the capital, unless otherwise stated. In addition their national railway, the Deutches Bundesbahn, is unsurpassed, and there are many good bus services as well.

CLAUSTHAL-ZELLERFELD
Location - 340 kilometers northeast of Bonn, and about 50
            kilometers northeast of Göttingen.
Train - From various places.
Road - From Bonn take the A59 north towards Köln, but skirt
            Köln to the east and join the A1 or E73 towards Wuppertal
            and continue towards Dortmund. Just west of Dortmund
            join the E63 towards Kassel. Just south of Kassel turn north
            along the E4 or A7 towards Göttingen. North of Göttingen
            turn off along the 241 to Northeim and follow this through
            Osteröde to Clausthal-Zellerfeld.

Clausthal-Zellerfeld is situated in the beautiful Harz Mountains not far from the border of East Germany. The town was the birthplace of the great German doctor and bacteriologist Robert Koch (1843-1910).

Robert Koch was contemporary with Louis Pasteur (see under France), and between the two of them they founded the concepts and techniques on which modern bacteriology is based. To put it in more meaningful terms they established the ideas which formed the basis for the conquest of infectious diseases.

Koch was born the third child in a family of 13, and his parents encouraged their children to learn and to travel. By the age of 5 he had taught himself to read and write, and before entering school he was an avid and knowledgeable collector of plants and animals. He did well at the local Gymnasium School, and at 19 he entered Göttingen University to study natural sciences. However, he soon transferred to medicine and was greatly influenced by the professor of physiology, Jacob Henle. No bacteriology was then taught in medical schools, but Henle firmly believed that contagious agents were living organisms, and there can be little doubt that this had a profound impact on Koch's mind.

He received his doctor's degree in 1866, and in 1867 married Emmy Fraatz, also from Clausthal. For five years after this the couple moved to a variety of places, but none suited them until they settled in Wollstein (now Wolsztyn, Poland), and it was here that Koch did the basic work which established him as one of the foremost scientists of his day. Whenever his practice would permit he spent his spare time at the microscope in his makeshift laboratory, and more and more began to observe bacteria. In particular, he started to examine the rodlike bacteria causing the disease anthrax in sheep, and with a stroke of true genius he cultured these (in vitro) using the aqueous humor of a cow's eye as the medium. The aqueous humor is the fluid in the chamber of the eye between the cornea and the lens, and is about as free from bacterial contamination as any living substance can be. Thus he was able to get a pure culture of the anthrax bacillus, something never achieved before. Later he used solid gelatin to ensure pure cultures. He described the whole life cycle of the organism, and demonstrated that when his pure cultures were injected into mice they did indeed contract anthrax. With this work he established the basic principles of bacteriology, which are still valid today; namely, that bacterial cultures must be pure to have any biological meaning, and that these pure cultures will produce a specific disease when injected into an appropriate animal.

Koch's work soon brought him recognition, and in 1880 he was appointed an advisor to the Imperial Department of Health in Berlin, and this became his permanent home. From Berlin, Koch's techniques rapidly spread throughout the world. He demonstrated that steam surpassed hot air and carbolic acid sprays (see Lister under England) in its sterilizing power, and thus revolutionized hospital procedures. In fact Koch's ideas of hygiene were soon applied to every aspect of private and public health, and are still in use today. Perhaps his greatest achievement of all came in 1881 when he isolated the tuberculosis bacillus, and demonstrated the disease could be transmitted by inoculation. It is almost impossible for us today to realize the scourge of tuberculosis, since in the last 100 years it has been virtually eradicated in many parts of the world, principally due to the pioneer work of Robert Koch. He tried unsuccessfully to use so called "tuberculins" to control tuberculosis. Its control had to wait for more modern techniques.

Koch did not confine his investigations to Berlin. Wherever there was epidemic disease, it was likely that he would be found there to investigate its causes at first hand. He studied cholera in Egypt and India, sleeping sickness in Africa, and malaria in New Guinea. In all cases preliminary controls were effected.

The latter half of the 19th century was a time of imperialist expansion, intense nationalism and rivalry between nations, particularly between France and Germany. It is really not surprising therefore that Koch as a German and Louis Pasteur as a Frenchman became embroiled in this, and their scientific judgements suffered the consequences. In addition Koch was not the easiest of men to deal with. He was authoritarian, often aggressive, and vicious in his criticisms of other people's ideas. Thus he had many enemies, and his reputation was not helped in 1893 when he separated from his wife to marry a young actress by the name of Hedwig Freiburg, with whom he had become infatuated. However, his scientific achievements were so great that his reputation survived all. He was awarded the Nobel prize for medicine in 1905, and died 5 years later a national and international hero. His ashes were deposited in his institute in Berlin.

The Birth House of Robert Koch
Osteröder Strasse 13 (corner of Bartelsstrasse)
Clausthal-Zellerfeld

This house was where Robert Koch was born. It is state property and preserved, but is privately occupied. There is an easily visible plaque over the front door which reads:

ROBERT KOCH
wurde am 12 Dezember
1843
in diesem Hause geboren.

Robert Koch House
Kronenplatz (near the Post Office)
Clausthal-Zelerfeld

This is the house where Koch spent his childhood, and like his birth house it is state property but privately occupied. A plaque over the front door reads:

In diesem Hause verlebte
ROBERT KOCH
seine Jungendzeit
1854 - 1862.

FRANKFURT-AM-MAIN
Location - 140 kilometers southeast of Bonn and one of the
          principle cities of Germany.
Train - From all major cities direct.
Road - From Bonn take the A3 or E5 towards Frankfurt and
        Wiesbaden, and exit at Frankfurt (there are many exits).

Frankfurt-am-Main is a huge industrial city, badly damaged during World War II but largely rebuilt. It was here that Paul Ehrlich (1854-1915) did much of the work that has so profoundly affected modern medicine.

Paul-Ehrlich-Institut
Paul-Ehrlich-Strasse 42-44
Frankfurt-am-Main

Opening hours:
        Normal business hours.
        No charge for admission.

Paul Ehrlich's place in the history of medicine, rests not on any one major discovery, but on the fact that his work laid the foundations on which modern hematology, immunology and chemotherapy are built. Through his demonstrations of the chemical reactions of dyes with living cells, hematology and later histology came into their own as sciences. Likewise his methods of assaying and standardizing antitoxins are still the basis of immunology. Finally he was the first person to produce a chemical substance which had meaningful chemotherapeutic effects. All remarkable contributions to biology and medicine.

Ehrlich was born of middle class parents in Strehlen (now Strzelin, Poland). His mother and father encouraged education, and by all accounts Paul was a happy and enthusiastic boy. He attended the local primary school, and at age 10 went to the Gymnasium in nearby Breslau. He entered the University of Breslau at 18 to study natural sciences, but soon transferred to Strasbourg University to study medicine. His student days at university were checkered, for he returned to Breslau and also attended Freiburg and Leipzig Universities, finally receiving his medical degree in 1878. However, before he graduated, he had already published his first paper on the effects of aniline dyes on living cells, and his doctoral dissertation was on the same subject. Fortunately the importance of his work was recognized at once, and upon graduation he was appointed to the research staff of the famous Charite Hospital in Berlin.

In Berlin, Ehrlich continued his research on the reactions of dyes on living cells, and gradually developed the fundamental concept that to understand biological processes, it would be necessary to describe them in chemical terms. The importance of this in the future development of biology cannot be overstressed.

In 1883 Ehrlich married Hedwig Pinkus, and the marriage proved extremely happy. They had two daughters to whom both mother and father were closely attached, and the family relationship no doubt helped Ehrlich in his somewhat troubled and insecure professional career. Shortly after his marriage he received an appointment at the Universiy of Berlin, but due to changes in those in control this did not last long. In 1889 he was without appointment, but set up his own private laboratory where for many years he conducted fundamental experiments in immunology. In particular he worked out methods for assaying toxins and antitoxins, and for determining their correct physiological doses.

As a result of this work, Paul Ehrlich's genius was once more recognized, and in 1899 he was made director of a new "Serum Institute" in Frankfurt-am-Main. Here he spent the rest of his active life, during which time he developed the first effective chemotherapeutic drug, Salvarsan. It was particularly effective against a bacterial group referred to as "spirochaetes," which includes the organism causing the deadly disease syphilis. Salvarsan can be described as a first step only, for it had many undesirable side effects, but it was effective enough that it gave hope for the future discovery of better chemotherapeutic drugs, and this has indeed proved to be the case, first with sulpha drugs and later penicillin (see under London and Fleming). He was awarded the Nobel prize in 1908.

Paul Ehrlich's great work "Die Experimentelle Chemotherapie der Spirillosen" (Experimental Chemotherapy of Spirochaetal Diseases) was published in 1910, and although the last 5 years of his life were personally happy for him, he was very distressed by the tragedies of World War I. He died in 1915 after a short illness. Paul Ehrlich was basically a simple man, who never sought fame or fortune, but his life's work has had a lasting effect on biology and medicine. He is buried in the Jewish Cemetery in Frankfurt.

Paul Ehrlich founded the institute which bears his name, and directed it for the last 15 years of his life. It is now owned and operated by the Ministry of Health and its function is the control and testing of vaccines. There is a small "memorial room" of Ehrlich memorabilia which is open to the public, and worthwhile seeing. It is also of great historical interest that although Paul Ehrlich was Jewish, he was so highly regarded by the German people that the Nazis saw fit not to rename Paul-Ehrlich-Strasse to suit their political ends.

HEIDELBERG

Location - 85 kilometers south of Frankfurt-am-Main.
Train - From many major cities direct.
Road - From Frankfurt-am-Main take the A5/E4 Autobahn
        south and then take the A656 turnoff to Heidelberg.

Heidelberg is one of the oldest and most picturesque towns in Germany. It is on the river Neckar, which is a tributary of the Rhine. Its origins are lost in time, but its famous castle (the Schloss) was begun as early as the 13th century, and its university was founded in 1385, making it one of the oldest in Europe. During the reformation the latter was a center of Calvinist doctrines, and the same was true of Nazi doctrines under the Hitler regime. However, after World War II the university was reestablished on traditional free academic foundations, and today it is one of the leading universities in

Germany. Fortunately, Heidelberg escaped any serious damage during World War II.

The University

The University of Heidelberg has throughout its history been noted for its achievements in areas other than natural sciences. Nevertheless, it would be a pity to miss it entirely for this reason. Its facilities are scattered, but much of the historical aspects are centered around the Gabengasse, and these are well worth a visit. In particular do not miss their famous library, with holdings going back many centuries.

Apotheken-Museum
Heidelberger Schloss
69 Heidelberg

Opening hours:
> Daily, 10.00 - 17.00
> Small charge for admission.

Apothecaries were the forerunners of the modern druggist. However, the transition was not a simple one. Very often they competed with physicians, and the two professions were often at odds. By modern standards most apothecaries would be considered quacks, but it must be remembered that their transition into druggists was completely dependent upon the development of modern chemistry, and this did not really occur until well into the 19th century. Be that as it may, "the wares and the arts" of the apothecary, throughout the ages, are a major part of medical history. Since apothecaries were an important part of society, there were many of them, and a lot of their materials have survived. Throughout Europe, and indeed in parts of the United States too, there are many apothecary museums, but none surpasses this one in the Heidelberger Schloss.

One has to climb the hill up to the castle to reach the museum, which is housed in a wing of a former Renaissance palace built in the middle of the 16th century by the Elector Palatinate Otto Heinrich. Other parts of the castle are much older, and the whole setting is very beautiful. The museum was founded in 1937, and opened to the public in Munich in 1938. There however, it was badly damaged in 1944 during World War II, and it was not until 1957 that it found a new home in its present location.

There are about 15 rooms, with displays going back four centuries. The historical knowledge and artistic abilities of the curators are outstanding, and in addition to the actual materials used by apothecaries, whole contemporary laboratories have been constructed. There is also a priceless collection of old and rare books on the apothecary's profession.

INGOLSTADT
Location - 80 kilometers north of Munich.
Train - From Munich direct.
Road - Take the A9/E6 Autobahn north from Munich and exit at
Ingolstadt.

The town of Ingolstadt, being on the Danube, has played a long and important role in the history of Bavaria, and fortunately escaped serious damage during World War II. What concerns us here is the history of the university, and particularly what survives in the form of an anatomy theater, which is now a superb medical museum. The University of Ingolstadt was founded in 1472, and the original building survives in the form of the Hoheschule in Goldknopfgasse. For 200 years the university was a leading educational institution. However, during the thirty years war (1618-1648) it suffered badly and went into decline, but rose again in the 18th century. In 1800 the University of Ingolstadt was moved, first to Landshut and then in 1826 to Munich, where it became the University of Munich.

Deutsches Medizinhistorisches Museum
Alte Anatomie
Anatomiestrasse 20
Ingolstadt

Opening hours:
April 1 - October 31, Tuesday - Sunday, 10.00 - 12.00
and 14.00 - 17.00. Closed Mondays.
November 1 - March 31, Tuesday, Thurday and Friday,10.00 -
12.00; Saturday and Sunday, 14.00 - 17.00. Closed
Mondays and Wednesdays.
Small charge for admission.

The Anatomy Theater of the University of Ingolstadt was built between 1723 - 1736, and it is the oldest north of the Alps. It was a major training place for medical doctors until 1800, when the university moved, and this magnificent building fell into private hands, eventually becoming a laundry! In 1930 it was rescued from complete decay, being purchased by the town of Ingolstadt, but it was not until 1969 that restoration was begun, with the subsequent establishment of a medical museum. In 1972 the University of Munich celebrated its 500th anniversary, and the following year the museum was opened. It is of interest to note that it is really the "brain child" of Dr. Heinz Goerke, a distinguished Munich physician, whose drive and dedication has created it in its present form.

The exterior part of the building is completely restored to its original form, and is most striking. At the back is a little courtyard garden, which was the original herb garden of the medical school. The historical displays are on two floors, arranged more or less chronologically, so that one gets a feeling for the whole historical development of medicine. Upon entering there are displays of Egyptian, Grecian and Roman medicine, and fascinating displays of "home medicine" in the 17th, 18th and 19th centuries. The displays are not confined to cases of instruments, as is so commonly the case, but include large pieces of medical apparatus such as autoclaves, iron lungs, anaesthetic machines, etc., including the original sterilizer from the laboratory of Robert Koch (see Clausthal-Zellerfeld). The second floor is mainly devoted to military medicine, which has played such a large role in the development of medicine in general. This is a medical museum in a lovely setting, with rich collections and a uniqueness of character with which the visitor will not be disappointed.

KAISERSWERTH
Location - 80 kilometers north of Bonn. It is a northern suburb of
              Düsseldorf near the airport.
Train - From Düsseldorf direct.
Road - From Bonn take the A555 north skirting Köln to the
              west and join the A57 north and then the A52 towards
              Düsseldorf. Cross the Rhine and then turn left (north) along
              route1 towards Duisberg. This leads past the airport (to the
              west) and straight into Kaiserswerth.

Kaiserswerth is a very old and beautiful town and is best known today for its famous nursing school, where no less a person than Florence Nightingale studied (see under London and Middle Claydon, England).

Diakoniewerk Kaiserswerth
Alte Landstrasse 121
4000 Düsseldorf 31

Opening hours:
>   Normal business hours.
>   No charge for admission.

A literal translation of Diakoniewerk is "service in the name of God," and it is an order of Protestant Deaconesses. In English it is referred to as The Institute of Protestant Deaconesses. The institute set in a large and beautiful park is an easy walk through the cemetery from the town center. It was founded in 1836 by Theodor Fleidner, and quickly became known for its dedication to nursing the sick, and eventually for training nurses. Florence Nightingale visited it twice, first in 1850 for two weeks, and again in 1851 for three months. The original hospital in which she studied still stands. It is called Altenheim Stammhaus and is at 32 Kaiserswerther Markt (corner of An St. Swidbert). Florence Nightingale was very impressed with the administration of the hospital, and the dedication of the deaconesses, but thought little of their sanitation procedures. In any case Florence Nightingale quickly became their most famous student, and her methods of sanitation soon found their way to the deaconesses.

The historical aspects of the institute are preserved in the archives of the library, presided over by Sister Ruth Felgentreff, who speaks fluent English. She is very enthusiastic, and delighted to show everything to interested visitors. Her treasures contain handwritten letters by Florence Nightingale and first editions of all her works, as well as many other interesting things. In 1975 a new 410 bed hospital was added to the complex and it has been named the Florence Nightingale Hospital. Inside the lobby is a lovely bronze bust of her. Of great interest also is the adjacent cemetery segregated into Protestant and Catholic sections! The Diakoniewerk Kaiserswerth has a major place in the history of nursing, and will not disappoint the historically-minded visitor.

MARBURG/LAHN
Location - 130 kilometers east of Bonn, and 80 kilometers
>   north of Frankfurt-am-Main.
Train - Direct from Frankfurt-am-Main, and many other cities.

Road - From Bonn take route 478 to Waldbröl and
Siegen. At Siegen take route 62 to Biedenkopf and Colbe,
and then turn south along route 3 to Marburg/Lahn.

Marburg is a very old and beautiful university town astride the
river Lahn, and fortunately escaped damage during World War II.
Today it is the home of the Behringwerke und Institut, which were
founded by the great German doctor Emil von Behring (1854-1917)
towards the end of the 19th century.

Behringwerke AG und Institut
Marbach
D-3550 Marburg/Lahn 1

Opening hours:
Normal business hours.
No charge for admission.

This enormous complex is at the village of Marbach, about 3
kilometers northwest of the center of Marburg/Lahn.

It is to Emil von Behring that we chiefly owe many of the
concepts of antitoxin therapy, and the control of the dread diseases
of tetanus and diptheria. He was one of twelve children in a
teacher's family in Hansdorf (now part of Poland). While at school he
developed his interest in medicine, but due to the poverty of his
family he saw little chance of ever becoming a doctor. However, one
of his teachers was able to have him admitted to medical school in
Berlin, on the condition that upon graduation he promise to serve in
the Prussian Army for 10 years. Behring accepted this and carried
out his promise. While still a student he began to think about the
problem of combating infectious diseases, and shortly after he
graduated he wrote a paper raising the question as to whether it
might be possible to "disinfect" the living organism internally as well
as externally, and he pursued this theme all his life.
In 1896 he married Else Spinola. It was a happy marriage and
he was devoted to his wife. They had six sons.
While in the army, Behring was sent to Berlin where he joined
the staff of the Institute of Hygiene and worked under its director,
Robert Koch (see under Clausthal-Zellerfeld). Here he also met and
collaborated with Paul Ehrlich (see under Frankfut-am-Main). On
completing his army service in 1889 he stayed on at the institute,
and it was here that he developed his brilliant ideas on serum

therapy and his theory of antitoxins. In good scientific fashion these theories were tested in the laboratory, and by 1890 he had proven that the blood of tetanus-immune rabbits possessed a substance which destroyed the tetanus toxin, and, most important, that this property was maintained when the serum of the rabbit was injected in other animals. The discovery made it possible to achieve therapeutic effects by serum transfusions. It was a giant step along the road to "internal disinfection." Behring coined the word "antitoxin" to describe this effect, and in due course reliable inoculations were developed for both tetanus and diptheria.

In 1894 Behring moved to Marburg/Lahn where he set up what is now known as the Behring Institut and continued his active research. He later established the Behringwerke. By this time he was being hailed as an international hero and honors increasingly poured in upon him. He was raised to the nobility, and in 1901 was awarded the first Nobel prize in medicine for his life's work.

At Marburg, Behring devoted himself to the fight against tuberculosis, although he admitted that he had little success. His later life was saddened by the horrors of World War I, but he was able to take some consolation in the fact that his tetanus vaccination saved the lives of millions of soldiers. He died in Marburg in 1917.

Behring's ideas and techniques have since been used to combat many other infectious diseases, and his name is certain to live as one of the great benefactors of mankind.

The Behringwerke is today a large corporation, with worldwide operations, manufacturing pharmaceuticals, and doing research mainly in various aspects of immunology. The Behring Institut is housed in the library, and comprises Emil von Behring's papers and other memorabilia concerning his life and work. This is all under the direction of Frau L. Zedlitz, the archivist, who is very cooperative. However, the "gem" is the so-called "Behring room" in another building nearby, and can be seen by request (in advance). Tours of the works are also available, but arrangements must be made well in advance. The "Behring room" itself is not the original office he occupied, but is an exact replica of it. Everything in it is the original-- his personal library, desk, furniture, pictures, etc. It is beautifully cared for, and truly a great experience to be in it. He is buried in a private mausoleum on company property, but his grave can be seen by request, again, in advance.

In Marburg itself there is also a monument to Emil von Behring, consisting of a head bust. It is set in a nice alcove, and located on

Pilgrimstein (at the corner of Deutschhausstrasse) opposite the side of the Elisabeth-Kirche.

Also associated with Emil von Behring, is his former residence "Villa Behring" (now offices and research laboratories of the University of Marburg), situated at Wilhelm-Roser-Strasse 2. It is off Ketzerbach, a few hundred meters from the Elisabeth-Kirche.

MUNICH
Location -190 kilometers east of Stuttgart.
Train - From many major cities direct.
Road - Take the A8/E11 direct from Stuttgart.

Munich is the capital of Bavaria and the principle city of Southern Germany. It lies astride the river Isar, a tributary of the Danube, and its origins go back to at least the 11th century. From then until now it has played a major role in the political, cultural and economic life of the area. Unfortunately Munich was severely damaged during World War II, and much of its tangible cultural heritage has gone. However, two major things survived, namely its university and the Deutsches Museum--the latter only just! Munich has a modern and magnificent railway system, the S-Bahn and U-Bahn, with its hub at the Hauptbahnhof.

Universität München
Leopoldstrasse
Munich

Opening hours:
    Normal business hours.
    No charge for admission.
U-Bahn-Universität.

The center of the University of Munich is located in the block at the corner of Schelling and Leopoldstrasse, but there are other parts of it scattered around the area. The origins of the university go back over 500 years, to when it was located in Ingolstadt. However, it is only in recent times that it has played a major role in the sciences, but it would be a pity to miss it on that account. The university is close to many of Munich's great art galleries, and the visitor will find much of interest there.

Deutsches Museum
Munich

Opening hours:
    Daily, 9.00 - 17.00. Closed on public holidays.
    Small charge for admission.
S-Bahn-Isartor.

The Deutsches Museum is one of the great science museums of the world, and is located on an island in the river Isar, with entrances off the Steinsdorfstrasse and Erhardtstrasse. Some of their priceless collections were severely damaged during World War II, but a remarkable job of restoration has been achieved.

As an introduction to the Deutsches Museum, we can do no better than quote from one of their guidebooks:

"The Deutsches Museum, which was founded in Munich in 1903 by Oskar von Miller (1855-1934), is a cultural and educational institution devoted to the whole field of exact science and technology. Its aim is to familiarize the widest possible public with the basic phenomena and laws of science and with the methods and tools of technology. It aims also to present visually the historical development of scientific knowledge and of its technical applications. The museum tries to achieve these objects by the display of originals and reproductions of historic apparatus and machinery and by means of models and demonstrations. Many of the demonstrations are either permanently working or designed so that they can be operated by the visitor. In many cases tools and machines are represented together with the workers using them. Reconstructions of factories and workshops, either full-scale or in the form of dioramas, give some conception of industrial conditions at various times. The Deutsches Museum not only presents German achievements, but also displays outstanding achievements of other countries. By showing that so many peoples have contributed to the growth of science and technology, it seeks to promote mutual understanding between nations."

Most of the displays in this extensive museum tend to be in the physical sciences and technology. However, many of them have played such a major role in the development of biology and medicine, that they are entirely relevant to the latter, and every visitor interested in the development of science cannot fail to appreciate them. There is, however, some biology, and a particularly fine "Hall of Fame" with portraits of many great scientists throughout the ages. There is also an extensive library in the history of science, which can be used by qualified scholars upon application to the librarian.

We cannot recommend the Deutsches Museum too highly. For what it is, it is unsurpassed in the world.

NEUSS

Location - 70 kilometers north of Bonn and 15 kilometers west of
          Düsseldorf.
Train - Direct from Düsseldorf.
Road - From Bonn take the A555 north, and skirt Köln to the west
          and join the A57 north. Exit at Neuss.

Neuss is a heavily industrialized town, but it was here that one of the founders of the cell theory was born--Theodor Schwann (1810-1882), and his memory is preserved.

In all probability the English scientist Robert Hooke (1635-1703) was the first person to see and describe "cells" as we understand them today. In addition, Jean Baptiste Lamarck (see under Paris) described them in 1809. However, it was a long time after this before the universal nature of cells as the basic unit of life was understood, and this discovery was made by Mathias Schleiden (1804-1881) and his compatriot Theodor Schwann. The importance of this discovery cannot be overestimated; it is one of the basic foundations on which all modern biology rests.

Schleiden was the son of a physician. He was born in Hamburg and spent his childhood there. At the age of 20 he went to the University of Heidelberg to study law. In 1827 he received a doctorate degree, and returned to Hamburg to practice law. However, he became deeply dissatisfied with the legal profession, finally abandoning it, and at the age of 27 he started in again at the university to study natural science, with a concentration in botany. At first he attended Göttingen and then Berlin where he met Theodor Schwann. Schleiden received his doctorate from Jena University in 1839, and although he stayed on there for a while, he had a restless nature and subsequently moved to Dresden and Dorpat.

In 1838 while still at Jena, and before he got his doctorate, he published a paper "Beiträge zur Phytogenesis" (Contributions to Phytogenesis) in which he clearly put forth the basic cellular nature of plants, and in 1842 this was elaborated in detail in his textbook

"Grundzüge der wissenschaftlichen Botanik" (Foundations of Scientific Botany). It is one of the great books in scientific history, establishing that plants are cellular, and set the stage for modern botany. This is the work for which he is remembered most, but he was a very prolific writer on a whole variety of subjects. He was also popular as a lecturer, and did much to improve the standards of education in the natural sciences. He died at Frankfurt-am-Main in 1881.

Theodor Schwann was a rather rare type of individual, who had a very short productive scientific career, while most of his life was spent in pondering religious problems and in teaching. He was born in Neuss, and by all accounts was a model child and very religiously orlented. In view of this it was assumed by all that he would enter the church, and at 16 he went to study at a Jesuit College in Cologne. However, the Jesuits did not quite have the expected effect on him, and he soon renounced theology to study medicine at the University of Bonn, and there he met for the first time the famous physiologist, Johannes Müller. Schwann went on to Würzburg and eventually Berlin where he received his doctorate degree in medicine in 1834. In the meantime Müller had also moved to Berlin, and upon receiving his degree Schwann immediately went to work in Müller's laboratory, and soon afterwards met Mathias Schleiden who was also working there. Müller, Schleiden and Schwann had an enormous influence on each other, and it was here between 1834-1839 that Schwann did his brilliant work culminating in the publication in 1839 of his book "Mikroskopische Untersuchungen über die Übereinstimmung in der Struktur und dem Wachsthum der Thiere und Pflanzen" (Microscopic Investigations Dealing with the Parallels of Structure and Growth in Animals and Plants).

Not only did this firmly establish the "cell theory" as we know it today, but Schwann argued for the theory in purely mechanistic terms. In so doing he made it plain that the theological theories of life were quite unnecessary, and that it was a phenomenon subject to the same laws as the physical sciences. Thus just as the cell theory is part and parcel of biology today, so also is the mechanistic view of life.

With the publication of this classic work, Schwann's productive scientific career was more or less over. He was violently attacked for his ideas, and quickly turned back to theology and teaching. In the same year as his great work was published he went to Louvain as a Professor of Anatomy, and finally in 1848 to Liège where his career was completed. The evidence suggests that he was a lonely and unhappy man all these years until his death in 1882. Nevertheless, Schwann's place in biological history is secure as one of the chief founders of the cell and mechanistic theories of life.

Unfortunately very little of the physical associations of Schleiden and Schwann survive. However, in Neuss there is a large bronze statue of Schwann. He is seated, and it is twice life-size. It is located in its own alcove at the entrance to the Hauptpost (main post office) at the corner of Neustrasse and Promenadenstrasse. The inscription at the base reads simply:

SCHWANN
1810 - 1882

We find it a pity that there is apparently no other tribute to Schleiden and Schwann.

REMSCHEID-LENNEP
Location - 60 kilometers north of Bonn and 30 kilometers east of Düsseldorf.
Train - Direct from Düsseldorf.
Road - From Bonn take the A59 north and skirt Köln to the east, then join the A1 or E73 towards Remscheid and Wuppertal. Exit at Remscheid-Lennep.

Remscheid-Lennep is a manufacturing town known for its textiles in the heart of the Ruhr industrial region. But above this it is famous as the birth place of Wilhelm Conrad Röntgen (1845-1923), the discoverer of x-rays, and in the town is a large museum dedicated to him.

Deutsches Röntgen-Museum
Schweimerstrasse 41
(near the Moll Platz)
5630 Remscheid 11 - Lennep

Opening hours:
Monday - Thursday, 10.00 - 17.00
Friday, 10.00 - 14.00, Sunday 14.00 - 17.00
Closed Saturdays.
Small charge for admission.

The director (1983) is Herr Ernst Streller and his secretary is Frau Erika Hamburg. They both speak English, and welcome visitors from foreign countries.

Wilhelm Röntgen was born at 1 Gänsemarkt (near the Moll Platz) on March 27th, 1845 and there is a plaque on the house to this effect. At the age of three the family moved to Appeldoorn in Holland, and here Wilhelm attended school, and at 16 he entered the Utrecht Technical School. Some minor thing happened to him here, which is not clearly understood, but the result was that he was denied admittance to the University of Utrecht. However, this did not stop him and he was soon admitted to the Polytechnic School in Zurich, Switzerland, as an engineering student. In 1868, at the age of 23, he graduated as a mechanical engineer, and the following year received his doctor's degree. At this time he became associated with the physicist, August Kundt, and in 1871 he followed Kundt to the University of Würzburg (see under Würzburg). The following year he married Bertha Ludwig. However, Röntgen did not at this time stay at the University of Würzburg, but went on to Strasbourg and Giessen, finally returning to Würzburg in 1888 as Professor of Physics. In 1894 he became Rector of the university.

Röntgen's momentous discovery was made in 1895 in his small laboratory in the Physics Institute, and it is of great interest that this was a case of "chance favoring the prepared mind," for the discovery was really outside his main field of research, which was the physics of solids. The moment Röntgen suspected he had observed a new phenomenon he concentrated wholly on it. Within six weeks he had demonstrated the extraordinary penetrating powers of the rays, had taken what we would now call x-ray photographs and observed the outlines in these of the bones in his fingers. He also took an x-ray photograph of his wife's hand. So clear and of such obvious importance was his discovery that before the end of the year he sent a short paper on it to the Physical and Medical Society of Würzburg. By January 1896 he was world famous, and a new tool for medicine was released which in many respects has revolutionized the science. Röntgen himself named his new discovery x-rays (they are called Röntgen rays in Germany), simply because they were unknown, and he clearly pointed out their potential uses in medicine, radiology, biology, physics, metallurgy, etc. Since then they have been applied in even more ways.

Not surprisingly, Röntgen quickly became a German national hero and was awarded the first Nobel prize for physics in 1901. But, as was characteristic of his nature, he gave the prize money to the

University of Würzburg. He also had no intention of seeking fame and glory, and was soon back in his laboratory studying the physics of solids. He wrote over 70 papers on physics, of which only 3 were on x-rays. He was always disappointed that the rest received little recognition! The later years of his life were clouded by World War I and the death of his wife in 1919. He himself retired in 1920 to his country house at Weilheim, near Munich, and died there in 1923. His name lives on in the rays he discovered, as does our debt to this modest man.

The Deutsches Röntgen-Museum was established in 1930 by a group of local doctors. However, it rapidly became so important that it was acquired by the town of Remscheid and is now responsible to a Board of Directors, comprised of distinguished citizens.

The displays are very extensive and educational, and are constantly added to by gifts from manufacturers of their latest x-ray equipment. The various rooms and displays include:

1. Röntgen's personal effects, including his many photographs taken on his travels in Europe.
2. Portraits of his family and other contemporaries.
3. Busts and original articles, letters, etc.
4. A reconstruction of a doctor's office circa 1905.
5. Röntgen's private library, also his lovely old desk and clock.
6. A reconstruction of Röntgen's laboratory at Würzburg.
7. Reconstructions of diagnostic treatment rooms with life-size displays and equipment.
8. Demonstrations of technical applications of x-rays.
9. Many others.

Röntgen's birth house is only 300 meters up the road and it is used as the museum's library and also as a guest house for visiting scholars.

In summary, we cannot recommend this museum too highly. Remscheid is also a pleasant place to spent a night while visiting the museum, and there is an excellent and comfortable hotel, the Berliner Hof, close by in the Moll Platz. A nice place to toast Wilhelm Röntgen and his legacy.

WÜRZBURG

Location - 100 kilometers east and slightly south of Frankfurt-am-
Main.

Train - Direct from Frankfurt-am-Main.

Road - Take the A3/E5 Autobahn from Frankfurt-am-Main to the east
and exit at Würzburg.

Würzburg, on the river Main, is one of the oldest cities of Germany, has been the seat of a Bishop since 741, and its university was founded in 1582. Despite the fact it was severely damaged in the final days of World War II, it is an extremely picturesque and facsinating old town. Of great interest to us, is that it was here in the University of Würzburg in 1895 that Wilhelm Conrad Röntgen (see also under Remscheid-Lennep) discovered the rays named after him, more commonly known as x-rays. The consequent impact of this discovery on both biology and medicine can hardly be exaggerated.

Physikal Institut
Universität Würzburg
Röntgenring 8b
87 Würzburg

Opening hours:
Normal business hours.
No charge for admission.

It was in this building in 1895 that Röntgen discovered x-rays. It is located on the Röntgenring close to the corner of the Koellikerstrasse. On the outside of the building is a large plaque which reads as follows:

In diesem hause
entdeckte
W.C. Röntgen
Im Jahre 1895
Die nach ihm
Benannten
Strahlen

which in translation reads: "In this building in the year 1895, W.C. Röntgen discovered the rays named after him." The actual room where the discovery was made is still there, but is now a modern physics laboratory. Permission to see it and other items of historical interest in the Physics Institute can be requested at the office. It is also possible to see the lecture room that Röntgen used. It is more or less the same as in his day. Of great interest also are three display cases containing some of Röntgen's equipment, etc. Amongst other things exhibited here are:

His Nobel Laureate Certificate;
His hunting gun, with a very early x-ray photograph of the loading breech;
An x-ray photograph of the hand of Professor G. Koelliker (Professor of Anatomy), and another of his wife's hand;
A commendation from the German Physics Society, signed by both Max Planck and Albert Einstein!

These are of great interest, but it should be realized that the main Röntgen Museum is in Remscheid-Lennep (see previously).

Institut für Geschichte der Medizin der Universität Würzburg
Koellikerstrasse 6, Rückgebaude
87 Würzburg

Opening hours:
Normal business hours.
No charge for admission.

It is perhaps a help to know that not far from the Physics Institute is the Institute for the History of Medicine, which is in charge of Professor Dr. Gundolf Keil, who is very knowledgeable about Röntgen. It is located slightly off the main street, behind some main buildings, and not easy to find - but persevere!

In concluding this chapter on Germany we would like to say that no doubt many people who read this may have their image of Germany tainted by the memories of two terrible world wars. Be that as it may, in recent years we have found Germany a magnificent and hospitable country to be in, and nothing can erase its great scientific tradtion and contributions.

Chapter 4

ITALY

It was in Italy that the Renaissance, or the revival of learning, began and it was not long after this before some of their best thinkers turned their attention to natural phenomena. Great centers of scientific learning grew up, particularly in Florence, Bologna, Pisa, Venice, Padua, and later at Naples. By far the most famous and promient Italian scientist has been Galileo Galilei (1564-1642). Although biology and medicine were not primarily his field of endeavour, his influence on all science was so great that we will have more to say about him. In the fields of biology and medicine, other Italians have played major roles. These include the Roman, Claudius Galen (130-200), Marcello Malpighi (1626-1694), Francesco Redi (1626-1697), Lazzaro Spallanzani (1729-1799) and others. Unfortunately nothing survives of their associations of which we are aware, and many of their important ideas have been superseded. Therefore we will devote this section of Italy to some of the traditionally great centers of scientific learning. It will also include an account of the anatomist, Andreas Vesalius (1514-1564), who although not an Italian, taught and did his major work at Padua.

With Italy's long and distinguished cultural history, going back to the Roman civilization and beyond, there is much more to see than just places of scientific interest, though often the latter are interwoven with the former. Italy has excellent roads in general, and their "Autostrada" criss-cross the country making it easy to travel relatively long distances in a short period of time. There are also many rail and bus services as well. Rome, on the river Tiber, is the capital, and it will be convenient for us to take this as a central point of orientation, though there are also many convenient routes into northern Italy from France, Switzerland and Austria. We feel compelled to warn visitors to Italy that the opening hours of their institutions are very variable, and in addition there is no guarantee that they will be open even during the stated times!

FLORENCE

Location - 315 kilometers northwest of Rome.
Train - From Rome direct.
Road - Take the A1 Autostrada north from Rome, and then one of
the many exits to Florence.

Florence, situated astride the Arno river, was an old Roman colony, and a military camp which Julius Ceasar built in 59 B.C. It became of some importance under the Carolingian Emperors, but it was in the 15th and 16th centuries, when under the rule of the Medici family, that it rose to supreme cultural heights. In large measure this has been maintained ever since. During World War II, allied soldiers approaching the city were told that "The whole city must rank as a work of art of the first importance." This accurately describes Florence, but it did not prevent terrible destruction. Some of Florence has gone forever, but today much restoration has taken place, and it is a very lovely place to visit. We cannot recommend too strongly a good historical guide book.

Before describing actual places of biological and medical interest in Florence, it will be well to give a short historical account of medicine in Italian universities, and Florence in particular. It is of great interest, and has something to teach us all.

During the Middle Ages, and starting about the 10th century, there was a school of medicine at Salerno, but no doctorate degree was given. Next in Italy came Bologna, first with law (1150) and then medicine. Art and music were also taught, but only law could receive a high degree. It was said that this was quite natural, because only law could be discussed, whereas medicine could not (i.e., the facts were known!). The man who eventually came to the defense of medicine was a Florentine, Taddeo Alderotti. He argued the case in Bologna, won the day, and about 1285 it became possible to award a high degree in medicine. This in fact may be considered the origin of medical degrees as we know them today. Padua started as a university in 1222, with a faculty of medicine, but no high degree. This was followed 22 years later by the founding of the University of Naples by Frederick II.

The University of Florence was founded in 1321 and at its inception there was a medical school. Unfortunately neither the university nor the medical school functioned very well, mainly because its founders were merchants, who bargained for the professors and always thought they were paid too much--times have scarcely changed! Later the students ran the university, and in many cases hired the professors.

In the middle of the 16th century, Cosimo di Medici turned all the students out of Florence and sent them to Pisa. Florence was of course his capital, and like many a ruler, before and since, he viewed students as a threat. However, the Hospital of Santa Maria Nuova, founded at the end of the 13th century remained, including its school of surgery. The system evolved whereby the students took 4 years of theory at Pisa, and then went to the hospital in Florence for two years of clinical work, at the end of which they received a master's degree in surgery.

In the 17th century some pupils of Galileo's founded what was primarily a scientific academy at the Court of the Medici. It was called the Academia del Cimento, and they met occasionally in the Pitti Palace. Lorenzo Bellini, Giovanni A. Borelli, Francesco Redi and Marcello Malpighi were all members of this academy, and exerted a major role in the advancement of science.

In the middle of the 18th century, the school of medicine at Florence was reformed by a professor of anatomy, Antonio Cocchi, and at the end of the century was again reorganized by the Grand Duke Pietro Leopoldo of Austria. The school was now "avant-garde", for it had courses in pediatrics, dermatology, psychiatry and the history of medicine. There was also a pediatrics hospital, which dated from 1420 as a home for foundlings.

In 1840 disaster struck the still surviving school of surgery, in the form of another tyrannical ruler, Leopold II, who closed it and ordered the students to do everything at Pisa. It was not until 1859, after the war of independence, that a private school of medicine returned to Florence and was finally recognized by the state in 1923, and incorporated into the University of Florence.

Instituto e Museo Storia della Scienza
Piazza dei Giudici 1
Florence

Opening hours:
>   Daily, 10.00 - 13.00 and 14.00 - 16.00
>   Small charge for admission.
>   Besides Italian, some guides speak a little English and
>   French.

This is an institute and museum of the History of Science, and is certainly one of the best in the world. It is situated near the Palazzo Castellani, on the banks of the Arno near the Ponte Vecchio, and adjoins the Uffizi Gallery. The displays in the museum are remarkably comprehensive and include biology and medicine, though they are heavily weighted in the history of physics and the work of Galileo (see under Pisa).

On the ground floor, where one enters, is an apothecary and chemistry (old chemistry) museum, also a collection of old clocks, including a pendulum clock attributed to Galileo. However, the main collections are on the first floor (second floor to us). These are displayed in 9 rooms as follows:

1. Mathematical instruments.
2. Mathematical and navigating instruments.
3. Geography and sundials.
4. Cosmography and geography.
5. The Galileo room, including lenses, telescopes and thermometers associated with him, and some of his written works in original editions.
6. Telescopes of the 17th and 18th centuries, and microscopes of the 17th century.
7. Microscopes from the 18th century to the present.
8. Telescopes of the 18th and 19th centuries.
9. Various mechanical instruments.

Also in the hallways are portraits of many famous scientists.

On the second floor (third floor to us) there are 10 rooms with the following displays:

1,2 and 3. These rooms are really a library of old and rare scientific books, ranging back to the 14th century. One cannot help but stand in awe as one looks at this superb and priceless collection.
4. Mostly the history of cartography, but also displays where instruments are matched to drawings in old books.
5. Lenses, including an incendiary lens of the 17th century, which both Sir Humphrey Davey and Michael Faraday came to Florence to see, in connection with their studies of the nature of fires.
6. Pneumatic instruments.
7. Electrostatic instruments.
8. Anatomy models.
9. Medical instruments and biological wax models.

10. Medical instruments.

This museum is under the direction of Professor Maria Luisa Righini Bonelli, and we cannot speak too highly of her expertise and achievements. We must note also that the museum carries on active research in the history of science, and tries constantly to expand its displays. Finally, we would warn the visitor to plan to spend some time here, as there is a great deal to see.

La Chiesa di Santa Croce
Piazza Santa Croce
Florence

Opening hours:
Variable, enquire locally.
This is an active church.

When Galileo died in 1642 he was buried in the churchyard of Santa Croce. However, 100 years later when the wrath of the church had somewhat died down, his body was transferred inside the church with a suitable monument, and this can be seen today.

Ospedale di Santa Maria Nuova
Piazza Santa Maria Nuova
Florence

Opening hours:
Normal business hours.
This is a working hospital.

This hospital was founded at the end of the 13th century, and interestingly enough the founder was Folco Portinari, the father of Beatrice, Dante's inspiration. It is one of the oldest in the world, and played a major role in the development of early surgery.

Ospedale di Pediatria
Piazza S. S. Annunziata
Florence

Opening hours:
Normal business hours.
This is a working hospital.

This hospital was originally a home for foundlings, and dates from 1420. The architect was Filippo Brunelleschi (1379-1446). The building also has some magnificent sculpture by Luca della Robbia (1400-1482). At the side of the main entrance there is a bell placed low down, so that it could be rung by children seeking help. It is a very beautiful and interesting place, and one of the earliest pediatric hospitals in the world.

Biblioteca della Facoltà di Medicina
Policlinico di Careggi
Viale Morgagni
Florence

Opening hours:
Normal business hours.
No charge for admission.

This is a magnificent medical library, particularly rich in early medicine in Italy. It can only be used by special permission of the librarian, but visitors can ask to see it, and the librarians are very helpful.

Museo Zoologica La Specola
17 Via Romana
Florence

Opening hours:
Variable, enquire locally.
Small charge for admission.

This museum has as its main display a very fine collection of biological wax models.

The visitor to Florence will of course want to see many more things than we have mentioned here, but in closing we would just like to suggest that you do not miss the Villa i Tatti, Via di Vincigliata. This contains the art collection and art history library of Bernard Berenson, left by him to Harvard University. It is a bit "out of the way," but more than worth the effort to get there. It is open Monday - Friday only, 9.00 - 13.00 and 14.30 - 18.00. Closed for the month of August.

NAPLES

Location - 220 kilometers southeast of Rome.
Train - From Rome direct.
Road - Take the A2 Autostrada south from Rome and then one of
the many exits to Naples.

The history of Naples goes back to at least 500 B.C. when it
was a Greek colony named Parthenope, and since then it has played
an increasing part in Italian history. It is the third largest city in Italy
with a population of over one million, a huge port, and set in
beautiful surroundings with a sub-tropical climate.

Stazione Zoologica di Napoli

Villa Comunale
Naples

Opening hours:
> Normal business hours.
> No charge for admission.
> This is an active research institution. But by application to the
> main office, permission to see over it is usually granted.

The Villa Comunale is a park (in the center of which is the
Stazione Zoologica) which borders the Via Caracciolo along the
seafront. The Stazione Zoologica (Marine Biological Station) at
Naples has played an enormous part in the development of all
modern biology, and no one interested in the history of biology and
medicine will want to miss it, not only for its historical significance, but
also for its massive and imposing architecture all set in a beautiful
park - regrettably often vandalized.

This marine biological station is by far the oldest in the world
and set the pattern for the future. It was founded in 1872 by the
young German doctor, Felix Anton Dohrn (1840-1909), who had
studied both medicine and zoology at a variety of universities, but
devoted his efforts to zoology. Anton Dohrn was "blessed" with a
very rich father, Carl August Dohrn, who liked to support scientific
research, and gave large sums of money to establish the station.
There were also many other founding donors, including Charles
Darwin. It was not exactly an accident that the foundation stone was
laid in 1872, for that was the year that the famous Challenger Deep
Sea Exploring Expedition set out, and as a result of the Darwinian
theory of evolution by natural selection (1859), many scientists were
devoting their efforts to marine life in attempts to trace its

evolutionary origins. At that time many were convinced that "ontogeny recapitulates phylogeny", i.e. that the embryological development of an individual animal recapitulates its evolutionary development. Thus it was thought that to explain evolutionary development, all that was necessary was to study embryological development. Unfortunately it did not prove that simple, but this was one of the main problems that early marine zoologists worked on at the station, and they soon found the many difficulties.

From the beginning the station's main function was marine biological research, and still is. Anton Dohrn also insisted that it should be highly internationally oriented, and that scientists from all over the world should come there to work and exchange ideas. A truly far-sighted and very productive concept which has advanced biological knowledge enormously. To give an idea of the scientific importance of this first marine station, it is only necessary to note that over 20 Nobel Laureates have worked there at one time or another. We mention simply a few: Jacobus Van't Hoff, Ilja Metschnikoff, Otto Warburg, Thomas Hunt Morgan, Otto Loewi, Albert von Szent-Gyorgyi, James Watson, Maurice Wilkins, George Wald and Karl von Frisch.

For most of its life (now well over 100 years) the station has been in private hands, but after World War II financial problems became so great that it was nearly forced to close. However, it is now under the direction of the Italian Ministry of Education, and it is hoped that better times are ahead.

Apart from the whole setting and structure of the station, there are two special things that the visitor should not miss. The first is the Marine Aquarium (one of the first in the world), which is currently (1984) undergoing extensive renovations. The second is the library, which apart from its up to date research holdings, is one of the best historical biological libraries in the world. The Archivist is Señora(Frau) Christiane Groeben, who is very knowledgeable and delighted to show visitors everything. In addition to her native German, she is fluent in Italian, French and English! She is also an excellent historian of biology.

The Stazione Zoologica di Napoli has a distinguished place in the history of biology.

PADUA

Location - 525 Kilometers north and slightly west of Rome. 30
      kilometers west of Venice.

Train - From Rome via Florence.

Road - Take the A1 Autostrada north from Rome, and follow this
      around Florence to Bologna. At Bologna join the A13, which
      skirts Ferrara and leads straight to Padua.

Padua is on the eastern side of the Valley of the Po in
Northern Italy. It claims its origin from Troy, but in any case it was
certainly an important town in Roman times. In 1337 it came under
the rule of the Carrara family, and was subsequently taken by Venice
in 1405. This had some influence on the cultural life of the city,
because Venice was not dominated by the church in Rome, and
Padua was able to establish centers of learning which were relatively
free of religious dogma. Padua was taken by the French in 1797,
and was ceded to Austria in 1814. It finally came under the rule of
the modern Italian state in 1866. It has been sacked, destroyed and
rebuilt many times over the centuries, but fortunately escaped major
damage during World War II.

Università degli Studi di Padova
Via Roma e Via 8 Febbraio
Padua

This is the central loction of the University of Padua, and the
main building here is universally called "Palazzo del Bo" (i.e., Ox
Palace) or just plain "Bo". The university is one of the oldest in the
world, with origins going back to the 13th century. What is so
important to us is that Galileo taught here, and during the 16th and
17th centuries it was the leading university of the world. This was
particularly the case for its school of medicine. It is a truism that there
can be no physiology without anatomy first, and it was during the
16th century in the medical school at Padua that human anatomy
was put on a modern footing. In fact, the University of Padua can
rightly claim to be the founding point of modern medicine. The
person principally responsible for it was Andreas Vesalius (1514-
1564).

Andreas Vesalius was of Flemish origin and born in Brussels
in 1514. His family was poor, but he managed to enter the arts
course at the University of Louvain, and in 1533 he went to the
University of Paris to study medicine. At that time Paris was one of

the leading medical schools, but like all medical schools of the day it was completely dominated by the "Galenic tradition," and to understand the revolution in anatomy brought about by Vesalius, it is necessary to understand what was meant by this tradition.

Claudius Galen (130-200) was the foremost medical doctor of ancient Rome, and became the private physician to the Emperor Marcus Aurelius. For his day, he was skilled in all branches of medicine and wrote over 80 treatises on the subject. None of these survive in the original, but only as copies. Until about the beginning of the 16th century they comprised the standard and accepted views on medicine, particularly the works on anatomy. This was unfortunate, because in Galen's day he was forbidden to dissect the human body and what his anatomical works consisted of was the anatomy of the barbary ape. For about 1000 years the anatomy of the barbary ape and human anatomy were considered one and the same!

As a student, Vesalius was taught Galenic anatomy. In 1536 he left Paris and returned to Louvain, where he was able to introduce human anatomical dissection into the medical curriculum. In 1537 he went to the University of Padua, still as a medical student, but so great was his knowledge that he was granted a doctor of medicine degree the same year, and the day after this was made an instructor in anatomy and surgery. He immediately introduced anatomical dissection into the curriculum. Even more importantly he did the dissection himself, rather than assign this important task to an assistant. Even though the number of human cadavers was very limited, he quickly learned that there were many differences between the anatomy of Galen and the realities of human anatomy, and he gave public lectures to demonstrate this. Very soon however, he was at work on what was to become a turning point in medical education, and by 1543 this manuscript was ready for publication.

Vesalius' great work was entitled "De Humani Corporis Fabrica" (The Structure of the Human Body). It was printed and published in Basle, Switzerland in 1543. It is really a magnifiecnt folio volume, and so accurate was it that it has often been said that medical students of today could learn their anatomy from this source without serious error. It is particularly notable for the standards of its illustrations. Traditionally these were said to have been done by the artist Jan Stephan van Calcar (c 1499-1550), who like Vesalius was Flemish, but this is not certain. However, there seems no doubt that they were done by students of the great Venetian artist Titian (1477-1576), and Calcar was one such student.

In retrospect it seems rather a pity that with the publication of "De Fabrica" Vesalius' academic career was over. The same year it was published, he left the university and entered the service of the Emperor Charles V. Later still he became physician to Philip II of Spain, and spent the last years of his life in Spain. In 1564 he went on a trip to the Holy Land, and on the return journey his ship was forced ashore on a small island. Vesalius died there shortly afterwards. His grave is unknown. Nothing can erase his great achievement, and with the publication of "De Fabrica" the premier place of the University of Padua in medicine was even more firmly established than ever.

Students of medicine came from all over the world, one of those being William Harvey (see under Folkestone, Britain).

Palazzo del Bo
Via Roma e Via 8 Febbraio
Padua

Opening hours:
> Daily, 10.00 - 12.00 and 14.00 - 16.00
> Small charge for admission.
> This may be seen by guided tour only, and lasts
> about one hour. The tour is in Italian.

At street level the Palazzo del Bo consists of a modern courtyard, built in this century, and it has fascist motifs on the walls. There are also plaques in memory of the university's war dead, all of whom "died for country and freedom"--it's the same the world over! Within is an inner courtyard, dating from the 13th century, and there is an interesting ritual carried out here every time a professor dies. His coffin is placed in the center of the courtyard, and is then ceremoniously lifted three times by the students in tribute to the professor.

Upon entering the building the first anteroom is called the Hall of Rectors. The walls are covered with frescoes by famous artists, a beautiful bust of Galileo who was a professor here for 18 years, and one of Copernicus (1473-1543) who studied medicine here from 1501-1503. Next is the impressive Great Hall (Aula Magna). It has been rebuilt many times, and the present one dates from the 19th century. On the walls are the coats of arms of the families of Rectors before the 16th century. In that century the custom was abolished. On the wall behind the main podium is the university's motto "Universa Universis Patavina Libertas" (Freedom to teach to everybody in Padua). The founders of the University of Padua were a group that broke away from the University of Bologna, where there was not freedom to teach. Despite this Padua, like so many other universities, has not always been able to live up to its motto.

After the Great Hall comes the Room of Forty. This is so called because on the walls are frescoes depicting 40 of Padua's famous foreign students. They include Nicolaus Copernicus (1473-1543), William Harvey (1578-1657), Sir Frances Walsingham (1530-1590), Oliver Goldsmith (1728-1774), etc. Also in this room is the original lecture podium, from which Galileo taught between 1592-1610.

Next is the Room of Medicine, and it is the original room built by the architect Morone in the 13th century. This is the main meeting room of the faculty of medicine, and the place where the medical students receive their degrees. A very fascinating tradition is preserved here. During the Inquisition in the 16th century, it was very difficult to obtain human bodies for dissection, but it was permitted to will one's body for this purpose. In consequence of this it became the custom for the professors of anatomy to leave their own bodies to the medical school. In honor of those who did, their skulls were preserved and to this day occupy a prominent place in the Room of Medicine!

After the Room of Medicine comes the world famous Anatomy Theatre. It was built in 1594 by Fabrizio D'Acquapendente, and is by far the oldest in the world. In was also the first of its type, and proved to be the prototype of all later anatomy theatres. The great anatomist, Giovanni Battista Morgagni (1682-1771), taught here for over 50 years. To us this theatre is a true "gem" in the history of medicine. One cannot help being impressed by its small size, the lovely clear lines of its architecture and the beautiful wood carving. Despite its small size there are standing places for 300 students. The circumstances surrounding its origin are very interesting. As explained previously, cadavers were hard to come by in the 16th century because of the Inquisition, which forbade their dissection. Thus the Anatomy Theatre was deliberately built over a small canal. Dissections were always done at night, in order to be as inconspicuous as possible, and in addition the cadaver was floated on a barge down the canal under the theatre and simply lifted from the barge right onto the dissecting table. The opposite could and did take place, for when the professor got word that the papal police were on their way, the body was swiftly handed down onto the barge again and floated away. Such were the perils of anatomy in the 16th century! The visitor is allowed to walk in the theatre, and one can lie on the dissecting table to get a "cadaver eyed view" of the scene!

The theatre was used until 1772, but since then has essentially been a museum piece. During World War II, it was taken apart and stored in a safe place. When it was reassembled after the war it was placed on a site slightly removed from the original.

There are several other historical rooms in Bo, but it is not necessary to describe them further. Of great interest, however, is a cafe just across the street from the main entrance of Bo. This is the famous Caffè Pedrocchi, which dates from 1831. It is of striking architecture and has played a large part in the life of medical students at Bo, the latter always having been highly elite and male oriented. Since the inception of the Caffè, there has been an interesting custom carried out each year by the graduating class of medical students. Upon leaving the Room of Medicine, where their degrees are awarded, they ceremoniously march across the road to the Caffè Pedrocchi, where they proceed to drink heavily, and each student in turn has to stand up on his chair and boast about his sexual exploits during his years as a student. It is said that some fantastic stories have been told here! Before leaving Bo, the visitor should walk over to the Piazza dei Signori and see the huge pre-Copernican Astronomical Clock, with the earth at its center, and the sun revolving around it.

Biblioteca Pinali
(Storia della Medicina)
Università Institute di Anatomica
Via Gabriele Falloppio 50
Padua

Opening hours:
>   By special arrangement (see below).
>   No charge for admission.
>   The Biblioteca Pinali is on the second floor of the Anatomical Institute at Via Gabriele Falloppio 50. However, the numbering of the street is confusing.

This is the old medical library of the university, with priceless collections of very ancient medical books--all beautifully maintained. Regrettably, the library is closed for lack of funds. However, by making special application of the Director of the Anatomical Institute, visitors are usually granted permission to see it. It is worth the effort.

Giardino Botanico
Via Orto Botanico 15
Padua

Opening hours:
   April 1 - September 30, daily 9.00 - 13.00 and 15.00 - 18.00
   October 1 - March 31, daily 9.00 - 12.00 and 14.00 - 16.00
   On all Sundays and holidays, 9.00 - 13.00 only.
   Small charge for admission.

These botanical gardens of the University of Padua are located near the Piazza del Santo, which is in the central part of the city. They were founded as part of the University of Padua in 1545 by an act of the Venetian Republic, and the original document still survives in the library. Their location, Renaissance layout and size are exactly the same as at the time of their foundation. At their inception the primary function was as a herb garden for the medical school, but even within the 16th century an Institute of Botany was founded with research as its main purpose, and this institute has played a major role in the development of scientific botany. It is interesting that Wolfgang von Goethe (1749-1832) visited these gardens in 1787 and this proved to be the inspiration for his work "The Metamorphosis of Plants". In addition to the gardens there is a magnificent library, which while not open to the public can usually be seen upon request to the librarian. The library is divided into two parts, the new and the old. The new is a modern botanical research library, but the old is a historical botanic library and one of the best we have ever seen. Its works go back to the 15th century, and its Linnaean collection is especially good. This library is beautifully and lovingly kept by its staff, who are also very knowledgeable. Repairs to their books are still done by monks in the local monastery.

Before leaving Padua, we can only hope the visitor will also take the opportunity to see its wealth of art, architecture and sculpture.

PISA
Location - 300 kilometers northwest of Rome.
Train - From Rome direct.
Road - Take the A16 Autostrada to the north and exit at Pisa. It may
   also be reached from Florence via the A11 Autostrada.

Almost everyone knows that Pisa is the home of the "Leaning Tower," but what is of far greater importance is that it was also the home of Galileo Galilei, one of the most influential scientists of all time.

Pisa on the Arno was originally a Greek colony, and is one of the many ancient towns in Italy, which through the centuries has suffered severely from the devastation of war (most recently World War II). At the same time, Pisa has managed to maintain a flourishing culture, and is a fascinating place to visit. It is regrettable that Galileo's birth place in Pisa is unknown, or perhaps does not survive, but fortunately there are still some direct associations with him.

Università di Pisa
Via XXIX Maggia 15
Pisa

Opening hours:
Nornal business hours.
No charge for admission.
This is Galileo's university.

Galileo will forever be remembered as the person, who more than any other, challenged and eventually overthrew a way of thought based on speculation and dogma, which was the hallmark of the all-powerful ecclesiastical authorities. For this he substituted the experimental method, and deductions therefrom, which has become the major means of all scientific research. As a result he narrowly escaped with his life! But Galileo did much more than that.

He was born in 1564, the first child of a middle class family. Much of his early education was private, and at 14 he entered a monastery as a novice, intending to become a priest. However, 3 years later in 1581 he left the monastery and entered the University of Pisa as a medical student. It seems he was not very interested in medicine but studied a great deal of mathematics, and left in 1585 without a degree. Four years later he was offered the chair of mathematics at Pisa and in 1592 went to the University of Padua (see elsewhere) where he found a much freer atmosphere for his work, which prospered. His time in Padua lasted 18 years, but in 1610 he went to Florence as a private mathematician to the Grand Duke of Tuscany. Most historians of the period agree that this turned out to be a disastrous move for Galileo, as Florence at that time was a rigid society, dominated by the Church, and it is not surprising that in the end Galileo was one of its victims.

Over his relatively long life span, Galileo's work and discoveries were vast, and we can only summarize them here. They included the discovery of the isochronism of pendulum oscillations, the equality of the velocities of falling bodies, the making of early thermometers and the refracting telescope, the latter making possible his astronomical observations and theories. He also very effectively applied mathematics to time and motion with undreamed of results. But, it was in 1632 that his greatest work was published. This was entitled "Dialogo sopra i Due massimi Sistemi del Mondo, Tolemaico e Copernicano" (Dialogue on the Two Chief Systems of the World, Ptolomaic and Copernican). Basically this book argued back and forth between the accepted Ptolomaic theory that the earth was the center of the universe and the heavenly bodies revolved around it, and the Copernican theory where the sun was central, and the earth was a planet revolving around the latter. Galileo's telescopic observations and his calculations had of course convinced him that the Copernican theory was the reality. The year after "The Dialogue" was published he was brought before the Inquisition in Rome and forced to renounce his ideas. He also was to remain "under observation" for the rest of his life, which however was still spent under the patronage of the Grand Duke of Tuscany. He died in Florence in 1642.

The main building of the University of Pisa is located on Via XXIX Maggio between the Piazza Garibaldi and the Piazza Dante. The University of Pisa is one of the oldest in the world, with origins going back to the 12th century, but its chief claim to fame is that here towards the end of the 16th century, Galileo was successively both student and professor. The facade of the building is of recent construction, but the internal courtyard and balcony, which are of superb architecture, were built in the 15th century. It is really a thrilling experience to see this, and realize that Galileo himself walked this same courtyard. The library, located off the courtyard, is very rich in old scientific books, and contains some original documents of Galileo. The library is not open to the public, but visitors may make their requests known to the librarian, who in our experience was cooperative.

La Cattedrale
Piazza del Duomo
Pisa

Opening hours:
Variable, enquire locally.
This is an active church.

The Cathedral of Pisa is of 11th century origin, and contains many magnificent works of art. However, from our point of view it contains the so-called "Lamp of Galileo." This is a great bronze chandelier strung from the ceiling of the cathedral. According to tradition it was while in church one day that Galileo observed the oscillation of the chandelier and subsequently established the isochronism of the oscillations of a pendulum. The tradition is quite possibly true, but in any case pleasant!

There are many other interesting things in the Piazza del Duomo, including the Leaning Tower.

Chapter 5

SWITZERLAND

As early as 1499 there was a confederation of the peoples in what is now Switzerland, and this can be considered the origins of the modern Swiss state. Despite the wars that have surrounded it, and been aimed at it, Switzerland has remained remarkably independent, with the exception of the French conquest by Napoleon Bonaparte in the early 19th century. This did not last long however.

Switzerland has always been a country where various nationalities and cultures have met, and its contributions and achievements have been enormous. In addition they escaped active involvement in both recent world wars, so that they have experienced little physical destruction. Thus there are some things of great interest to be seen in the history of biology and medicine. The capital of the confederation is Bern, but there are other major cities from which visitors may more easily orientate themselves. Despite its mountainous terrain, the roads and railways are excellent.

BASEL
Location - 90 kilometers north of Bern.
Train - From Bern and other cities direct.
Road - Take the N2 Autobahn north from Bern.

Basel is at the point where Switzerland, Germany, and France meet, and is at the head of the Valley of the Rhine. Because of its location, Basel has for a long time been a crossroad of commerce. From our point of view, however, it is of great interest that in the 16th century Basel became the foremost printing center in the world, and it was here in 1543 that Andreas Vesalius (see under Padua, Italy) came to have printed his great anatomical work, "De Humani Corporis Fabrica". Basel has since been superseded by other printing centers, but fortunately Vesalius left his mark.

Anatomisches Museum
Anatomisches Institut
Universität Basel
Pestalozzistrasse 20
Basel

Opening hours;
    Weekdays, 10.00 - 16.00
    No charge for admission.

This is a teaching museum of anatomy, and can be seen only by permission of the director of the institute. However, this is usually granted, if it is not in use. Of special interest in this museum is a human skeleton, which Andreas Vesalius dissected as a demonstration for medical students when he visited Basel in 1543, and then presented it to the university. It is perhaps the oldest surviving human dissection in the world. It has been somewhat "beaten up" through the centuries, but there is no doubt it is the original. It is marked as follows:

"Männliches Skelett das der Meister der Anatomie Andreas Vesal aüs Brüssel der hiesigen Universität schenkte als er 1543 sich in Basel auf hislit, in den Druck seines grossen anatomischen Werkes zu Cesorgen."

In translation this reads:

This skeleton was given by the master of anatomy, Andreas Vesalius of Brussels, to this University, when he stayed in Basel in 1543 in order to attend to the publication of his great anatomical work.

Medizinhistorische Bibliothek
Institut für Pathologie
Schönbeinstrasse 40
Universität Basel
Basel

Opening hours:
Weekdays, 9.00 - 17.00
No charge for admission.

This is a magnificent medical historical library, and may be seen by permission of the librarian. It would be a pity to miss it while in Basel.

GENEVA
Location - 170 kilometers southwest of Bern.
Train - From Bern and other cities direct.
Road - From Bern take the N12, N9 and N1 Autobahns via
Lausanne to Geneva.

Geneva is situated at the west end of Lake Geneva and is said to have one of the most beautiful locations of any city. It has a long cultural history, and is a very pleasant place to visit.

Musée d'Histoire des Sciences
Villa Bartholoni
128 rue de Lausanne
Geneva

Opening hours:
April - October only. Daily, 14.00 - 18.00
No charge for admission.

This is a small but excellent museum of the history of science, set in a park on the shores of Lake Geneva. Of its many exhibits two are of great interest in the history of medicine and biology:

1. A very complete and comprehensive collection of micro-scopes and other optical instruments going back to the 17th century. There are also other physical instruments as well.
2. A good collection of medical instruments going back to the 18th century. Also particularly fine collections of

medical apparatus related to high altitudes, early
barometers, thermometers, hygrometers, etc.

ZÜRICH
Location - 120 kilometers northeast of Bern.
Train - From Bern direct.
Road - Take the N2 Autobahn north from Bern, and then branch on
to the N1 to Zürich.

The origins of Zürich go back to Roman times, but more
recently it has become the major commercial center of Switzerland,
with a culture to match it.

Medizinhistorisches Museum
Universität Zürich
Rämistrasse 71
Zürich

Opening hours:
Mondays and Thursdays, 14.00 - 17.00
Saturdays, 10.00 - 12.00
Small charge for admission.
Rämistrasse 71 is the main building of the University of Zürich,
and the historical medical museum (also called "Oeffnungszeit
Museum") is on the 4th floor.

It is really remarkable how few good historical medical
museums there are, but this is certainly one of them! It is large, rich
in its collections, and the exhibits have been displayed by experts
with a "loving hand." Virtually everything is in glass cases, easily
seen and carefully labeled, so that even a person with no medical
knowledge can get a great deal from the displays. We think it
important to give an idea of the comprehensiveness of this
museum, so some of the displays are listed below.

1. Early medicine in Africa.
2. Early Christian medicine.
3. Ancient Egyptian medicine, with copies of the Ebers
papyrus and other medical treatises.
4. Ancient Peruvian medicine.
5. Ancient Roman medicine.
6. Skeletal models showing tremendous progress around
1550.

7. Comparison of teaching models from 16th, 17th, and 18th centuries.
8. The switch of emphasis from anatomy to physiology in the 19th century.
10. Collections of stomach pumps, syringes and instruments used for tapping in pleurisy.
11. Apparatus from psychiatrists' clinics of the 19th century.
12. Superb collections of old medical books going back to the middle ages, which are displayed.
13. Comparison of the anatomy of Vesalius (1514-1564) (see under Padua, Italy) and Eustachius (1524-1574) with skeletons of the 15th century. This demonstrates a marked and sudden change for the better in the 16th century.
14. Surgical instruments of all types from many centuries.
15. Instruments for treating wounds.
16. The development of crutches, artificial limbs, etc.
17. History of anaesthesia apparatus.
18. Displays devoted to Louis Pasteur (see also under Arbois, Dôle and Paris, France) and Joseph Lord Lister (see also under Glasgow, Scotland).
19. Early x-ray apparatus and photographs.
20. Instruments and illustrations for cataract operations.
21. Development of spectacles in the 18th and 19th centuries.
22. Early iron lungs
23. Extensive collections of dental instruments.
24. Displays illustrating the development of obstetrics, including lying-in rooms and childbirth chairs.
25. History of goiter.
26. History of syphilology.
27. History of tuberculosis.
28. Complete display of an apothecary's shop.
29. An original coffin of the 14th century with a hinged bottom. This has a grim history. At the time of the great plague, deaths were so frequent and coffins in such short supply, that they were made with hinged bases. The dead person was put in the coffin, which was then transported to the cemetery and placed over the grave. The bottom was opened, the body fell into the grave and the coffin simply used again.
30. Portraits and short accounts of famous doctors.

There are many more displays in this superb museum, and we cannot recommend it too highly.

Medizinhistorisches Institut der Universität Zürich
Rämistrasse 71
Zürich

Opening hours:
　　Weekdays, 9.00 - 17.00

In the same building as the medical museum is an Institute for the History of Medicine, and is well worth a visit in conjunction with the museum. There is a superb library on the history of medicine, as well as some very rare old medical works. It can only be used by qualified scholars, but visitors can ask permission of the librarian to see it.

Chapter 6

AUSTRIA

Austria, like its neighbor Switzerland, is one of the smaller mountainous countries of central Europe. Before World War I it was part of the huge Austro-Hungarian Empire, and for a short time before and during World War II it became an integral part of Germany. However, it emerged from this latter struggle as a modern independent state.

Austria has always had a society of high culture, centered on its capital, Vienna, astride the banks of the Danube. From our point of view, however, it is important that medicine flourished here, particularly in the 19th century, when medical students from all over the world came to Vienna if possible. Vienna is still a leading center of medicine, and there is much of historical interest that survives.

VIENNA
Location - At the eastern end of Austria, and about 450 kilometers
from Munich in southern Germany.
Train - From many parts of Europe direct.
Road - From Munich take the E11 Autobahn to the east, and at
Salzburg join the E14 to Linz, and finally the E5 to Vienna.

Institut für Geschichte der Medizin der Universität Wien
Josephinum
Währinger Strasse 25
Vienna

Opening hours:
Monday - Friday, 9.00 - 16.00
Small charge for admission.

This is an institute for the history of medicine and is part of the 600 year old University of Vienna. However, as an institute it is unique in having one of the best medical museums in the world.

The Josephinum, where the institute and museum are housed, was built about 1785 at the command of the Emperor

Joseph II (1741-1790) -- who is generally considered by historians to have been an "enlightened monarch". The building was constructed to house an academy for the formal training of surgeons, mostly for the benefit of the army. Still, this was one of the first formal schools of surgery and from which part of the excellence of Viennese medicine derives. It is important also that the Josephinum is considered one of the most beautiful buildings in Vienna, the architect having been an Italian, Isidore Canevale (1730-1786).

As early as 1850, there was a chair of the History of Medicine at the University of Vienna, but it was not until 1920 that the great historian of medicine, Max Neuburger (1868-1955), transferred the History of Medicine Institute to the Josephinum and also established the museum there. Fortunately both have prospered, and today it is a great experience to visit the Josephinum.

The museum is large and we can only highlight its main exhibits here. First and foremost is the huge (1192 specimens!) "Collection of Anatomical and Obstetric Wax Preparations." This collection, commissioned by Joseph II, was modeled in Florence from the wax of wild bees between 1775-1785, and for many years subsequently, was the means by which army surgeons learned their anatomy. The happy combination of artistry and accuracy in the wax models is truly remarkable, and it is difficult to put into words their visual effect. They are all in cases of handblown glass inlaid in rosewood. Two centuries of wear and tear have taken their toll, but fortunately the whole collection is being gradually and meticulously restored.

Other main exhibits in the museum show the development of medical teaching, ophthalmology, hygiene, brain function, surgery, pathology, blood grouping and many more. Also the early development of many modern medical instruments, much of which took place in Vienna. As we have stressed this museum is extensive, and many interesting hours can be spent there by a casual visitor.

Finally in this Institute of the History of Medicine is a magnificent historical library of medicine. Some of its holdings go back to the 15th century, and it has virtually every major medical work published since then. The library can be used only by professional scholars, with the permission of the librarian, but visitors can ask to see it. The library also has an extensive collection of medical manuscripts and portraits of famous doctors. Few people could fail to be impressed with this institute, and the role it plays in the culture of Austria and the world beyond. We were particularly impressed with the superb care of everything and the dedication of the staff.

Sigmund Freud Haus
Berggasse 19
Vienna

Opening hours:
> Monday - Friday, 10.00 - 13.00
> Saturdays, Sundays and holidays, 10.00 - 16.00
> Small charge for admission.

Sigmund Freud, the founder of psychoanalysis, lived and worked in this house from 1891-1938. It is now maintained as a museum (see also under London, England).

So much controversy, a great deal of which has been ridicule and misunderstanding, has surrounded the work and achievements of Sigmund Freud (1856-1939), that his name still conjures up sarcasm and derision. But there can be no doubt about his permanent place in medical history.

Freud was born in Freiberg, Moravia, now called Pribor and part of modern Czechoslovakia. His family was poor. When he was only 4 they moved to Vienna, and this became his home for most of his career. Freud was a keen student, and his family encouraged learning. He graduated with distinction from the gymnasium, and at 17 entered the University of Vienna to study medicine. It took him 8 years to get his medical degree, mainly because he devoted much of his time to medical research rather than pursuing the prescribed curriculum. However, in 1881 he got his degree and joined the staff of the famous Allgemeines Krankenhaus, where he specialized in neuropathology. In addition to his clinical activities he carried out research on the anatomy of the human brain. At this period in his life he is said to have become addicted to cocaine which he found enabled him to work well. If this was the case he was apparently able to give it up later.

After a short study trip to Paris, Freud set up practice in Vienna as a neuropathologist, and in the same year, 1886, he married Martha Bernays who became his life long companion. With the beginning of his private practice, Freud also started active research into what we now call psychoanalysis. Fortunately he was on the staff of the medical faculty of the University of Vienna, which gave an outlet for his very new, and to some people "alarming", ideas.

During the years which followed, Freud made known his theories and ideas in various books and journals. It is generally considered that the most important book he wrote was "Die Traumdeutung" (The Interpretation of Dreams). This came out in 1900, and contains all the basic concepts of psychoanalytic theory and practice - the erotic nature of dreams, the "Oedipus complex," the libido and many others, all related to the subconscious. It was greeted with a storm of hostility and abuse, which has not yet died away, but the book has survived as one of the great works of medicine. Obviously some of Freud's ideas have been superseded, but considering that he was dealing with something so complex as the human mind, it is remarkable how accurate he has proved to be.

At the age of 67 and at the height of his fame and career, Freud developed cancer of the jaw. For the rest of his life he was a martyr to this. He underwent many operations, suffered severe pain and eventually died from it. The last years of his life were saddened by the coming of the Nazi regime in Germany. Freud was Jewish, and when the Nazis took over Austria in 1938 he and his family had to flee to England where he found sanctuary (see under London, Hampstead). He died there the following year. He was 83.

The Sigmund Freud Museum is on the mezzanine floor of Berggasse 19. It was here that he lived and worked. The museum consists of 4 rooms. The first of these was the waiting room for his patients. This contains the original furniture, and was restored with the help of his daughter, Dr. Anna Freud, who knew it well. The second room was his consulting room, which was almost perfectly soundproofed. Much of the original furniture of this room is in London, but photographs on the walls clearly depict everything as it was when in use. The third room was the sitting room of the family, and contains mementos of many episodes in Freud's life. Finally there is the foyer, where there are now books, portraits, etc. for sale. There are other rooms here which he occupied, but they are not open to the public.

A visit to the Sigmund Freud Haus brings one in close touch with a man whose legacy has benefited millions of people in trouble, and whose name is likely to live as long as humans survive.

Allgemeines Krankenhaus
Alser Strasse 4
Vienna

Opening hours:
>Normal business hours.
>This is an active hospital.

This is the Vienna General Hospital. It is an enormous complex today, and has in the past played a huge role in the development of modern medicine. It was founded in 1693, but the main buildings date from the 18th century. It was here that Ignác Semmelweis (see under Budapest, Hungary), Sigmund Freud and many others worked. This was also the center of the great period of Viennese medicine in the 19th century. Obviously one cannot visit the wards, clinics, etc. of the hospital, but one can walk through the enormous and very lovely courtyards.

Universität der Wien
Dr. Karl Lueger-Ring
Vienna

Opening hours:
>Normal business hours.
>No charge for admission.

This is the main building of the University of Vienna. It is worth a visit, simply because it is one of the great universities of the world where many famous doctors, etc. have studied and taught. Nearby is the Dr. Ignaz Seipel-Platz where some of the buildings of the "Old University" survive.

In conclusion we must point out that Vienna is famous not only for its medicine, but perhaps above all for its music, and the visitor will surely want to see some of the many interesting places in the history of music.

Chapter 7

CZECHOSLOVAKIA

Czechoslovakia is one of the smaller countries in central Europe with a checkered history. Before World War I it was an integral part of the Austro-Hungarian Empire, but upon the latter's dissolution after the war, Czechoslovakia was created as an independent state. It was occupied by Germany during World War II, but was eventually liberated by the allied armies and regained its independence. However, it shortly came under the domination of the U.S.S.R. and this is still the situation today. From our point of view there is one place of major interest in the history of biology and medicine in the city of Brno, which is where Gregor Mendel (1822-1884) established the modern science of genetics. We feel compelled to point out that crossing the border into Czechoslovakia is not exactly easy for a westerner, and it is of the utmost importance that full preparations are made in advance. Nevertheless, once inside the country there are reasonably good roads and train services between the major cities. We found the people pleasant, cooperative and eager to help.

BRNO
Location - 200 kilometers east and slightly south of the capital
Prague.
Train - Direct from Prague.
Road -   Take the E14 from Prague and exit at Brno. There is
another way of getting to Brno by road, which may be more
convenient for many people, and this is from Vienna in
Austria. Brno is about 135 kilometers north of Vienna and
the E7 runs straight between the two cities. There is also a
good bus service two or three times a week between Vienna
and Brno, and we found this helpful, as it avoids all the
problems of taking a car across the border. Brno was
formerly called Brünn, its German name, and has been
famous for a long time as a textile center. It is large, but
there are reasonably good public transportation services.

188

Mendelianum
Mendlovo Namesti
Brno

Opening hours:
Tuesday - Sunday, 9.00 - 16.00
Closed Mondays.
Small charge for admission.

This is part of the Augustinian monastery, where Mendel lived. It comprises a Mendel museum and library, and also the garden where he performed his genetic experiments.

Johann Gregor Mendel was born in 1822 in Heinzendorf, Austria (now Hyncice, Czechoslovakia). His mother and father were both peasants, but from families with long traditions of professional gardening, and young Johann was brought up in this tradtion. He was a good student at school, but suffered from severe mental strain which plagued him all his life. In due course he entered the University of Olmutz to study philosophy, which fortunately for his later work included a considerable amount of mathematics.

In 1843, at the age of 21, he entered the Augustinian monastery in Brno, taking the name of Gregor. Here he found an atmosphere conducive to learning, and as part of his theological studies between 1844-1848, he attended courses at the Philosophical Institute in such things as pomology and viticulture. Later under the auspices of the monastery, Gregor went to the University of Vienna and studied more botany. Due to illness he never received a degree from Vienna, and returned to the monastery which, with minor interruptions, was home for the rest of his life.

Mendel began his work on the hybridization and cross pollination of plants in 1856. It took him 10 years of careful and painstaking work, mostly on garden peas, to unfold the basic phenomena of what was to become the new science of genetics. The language Mendel used to describe his results is no longer current in genetics, but basically what he established for peas was as follows:

1. There was in each plant a pair of hereditary factors controlling flower color and other characteristics.
2. The two factors in each pair are derived from the plant's parents, one member of the pair from each parent.

189

3. The two factors in each pair separate during the formation of germ cells, so that each germ cell receives only one factor.
4. The factors for the various characteristics (e.g., red or white flowers) are alternate forms of the same factor, one being dominant over the other.

All this has since evolved into the modern concepts of genes, alleles, homozygotes, heterozygotes, etc. and the science of genetics, with its incredible achievements and benefits, to say nothing of its basic contribution to the understanding of biology itself.

Mendel published his results in 1866 in the journal of the local Natural History Society, under the title "Versuche über Pflanzen-Hybriden" (Experiments in Plant Hybridization). Here fate took an unfortunate hand, for there were only 20 copies printed (only 6 are known to survive) and apparently the local readers of the journal did not understand the significance of the work. The journal had such a narrow distribution that it never reached the main centers of science. Thus his work "lay dormant" for 36 years before it was rediscovered in 1900 and finally put to use. It is really impossible to overestimate the importance of Mendel's work, it was a triumph of preparation and perseverance.

In 1868 Mendel was elected Abbot of the monastery, and the official duties involved with this occupied an increasing amount of his time. With the exception of some work on the hybridization of bees, only spasmodically did he do any more scientific work. He died at the Augustinian monastery in 1884.

To return to the monastery itself. It is no longer used as a monastery, but it is very much intact as Mendel would have known it. There is a huge garden courtyard to the monastery building, but the actual garden that Mendel used is a small fenced area right at the entrance to the Mendel museum. Like everything else at the Mendelianum, they are beautifully kept and are a joy to see. Inside the building there are several rooms which comprise the Mendel museum. The first of these is the Mendel memorial room. Originally this was the dining room of the monastery, but it is now fitted out with a series of panels explaining Mendel's life and work. There are also display cases showing his own instruments, microscopes, grafting tools, pressed plants, etc. Next there is the Abbot's room. This was the conference room of the monks, and it is preserved more or less intact as it was originally. It is a lovely room with superb furniture and various large portraits on the walls. There is also a library section in the museum, which contains many of Mendel's personal books. It is of great interest that amongst these is an early German edition of "The Origin of Species, etc." by Charles Darwin. It is really one of the tragedies of 19th century communication, that Mendel knew of Darwin's work, but Darwin did not know of Mendel's, which was something Darwin desperately needed to explain certain aspects of his evolutionary theory. There are other rooms occupied by the director and his staff.

When Mendel died in 1884 he was buried in the Abbots' plot of the Central Cemetery in Brno. The Abbots' plot is difficult to find, and some assistance will be necessary, but once there Mendel's simple grave is clearly marked. Lovers of music may also wish to see the grave of the great Czechoslovakian composer, Leos Janacek (1854-1928), in the same cemetery.

Brno, Czechoslovakia, is not the easiest place to get to, but for dedicated geneticists, doctors, biologists, historians of science, etc., the effort is worth it. It is a pleasant thought that in Brno there is this permanent and cherished memorial to Gregor Mendel, which we hope will remain in good hands.

Chapter 8

HUNGARY

Hungary lies due east of Austria, and like the latter was part of the Austro-Hungarian Empire before World War I. However, after that conflict it became an independent state and remained so until World War II, when it was occupied by Germany. It was liberated by the U.S.S.R. in 1945, and has remained in close association with the latter ever since. From our point of view it was in Budapest that the great 19th century physician, Ignác Philipp Semmelweis (1818-1865) was born. This event is commemorated by a very good medical museum there. It is important that we point out here, that crossing the border into Hungary is relatively easy as compared to crossing into its neighbor Czechoslovakia. A visa is required, but it is not hard to get, and there are a minimum of formalities at the border.

BUDAPEST
Location - 260 kilometers east and slightly south of Vienna.
Train - Direct from Vienna and many other cities.
Road - Take the road east out of Vienna towards Batislava, but at
       Schwechat take the right fork to Bruck and the Hungarian
       border. Inside Hungary, pick up Route 1 to Gyor and
       Komarno. Then follow Route 10 to Budapest. There is,
       however, another, and in our opinion a much more pleasant
       way to reach Budapest. That is to take the hydrofoil from
       Vienna down the Danube to Budapest. It goes daily and
       takes about 5 hours. It is a very comfortable and remarkably
       beautiful journey, which we cannot recommend too strongly.
       Budapest consists of the twin towns of Buda and Pest, and
       is one of the major cities of eastern Europe with a long and
       important history, closely associated with the ups and downs
       of the Austro-Hungarian Empire. It suffered severe damage
       in the final days of World War II, but much of this has been
       repaired, and today with its location on both sides of the
       Danube, it is really a very impressive city and a pleasant place
       to visit.

Semmelweis Medical Historical Museum
I, Aprod U. 1-3
Budapest

Opening hours:
>Tuesday - Sunday, 10.00 - 16.00
>Closed Mondays.
>Small charge for admission.

This museum is on the Buda side of the Danube, and situated at the base of the hill on which stands the former Royal Palace.

Ignác Semmelweis was born in 1818 into a lower middle class family in Buda. He received a reasonably good elementary education at the Catholic Gymnasium in Buda. He later attended the University of Pest, and finally received a medical degree from the University of Vienna in 1844. At that time Vienna was a major center of medicine, and Semmelweis was determined to stay there. It was fortunate for the future of medicine that he did, and he managed to get an appointment in one of two obstetrical clinics in the Vienna General Hospital (see under Vienna, Austria).

Here a situation existed which seems almost incredible today. The first clinic, to which Semmelweis came, was operated as a teaching clinic for medical students, and in this the maternal death rate was over 13% from puerperal fever. This is now known to be an infectious disease of the female reproductive tract, commonly called "childbed fever," but in those days its cause was unknown and the outcome was nearly always fatal. The second clinic in the hospital was run by midwives and for the teaching of midwives. Here the death rate from puerperal fever was only 2%. This was in 1847 and everyone was baffled by the phenomenon, but Semmelweis made a crucial observation and deduction. The observation was, that in the first clinic the medical students went straight from the autopsy room (where they did anatomical dissections on cadavers) to the obstetrical clinic where they examined patients, without any washing of hands on the way! This of course was not the case in the second clinic operated by midwives, and Semmelweis concluded that the medical students were in some way carrying the infection to the patients. Consequently he ordered that everyone attending an obstetrical case should first wash their hands in a solution of chlorinated lime. This seems almost common sense today, but it represents one of the great steps in the development of modern medicine. The results of this procedure were dramatic, for within one month the death rate in the first clinic dropped to that in the second.

One might have thought that with such conclusive evidence of success, Semmelweis' ideas would have prevailed, but it was not the case. This was before the time of Louis Pasteur's (see under France) theories on the microbial nature of infectious diseases. Today, Semmelweis is generally considered the direct precursor of Louis Pasteur. His ideas were not welcomed by the conservative medical community in Vienna, and he was even laughed at and ridiculed.

The rest of his career is really insignificant. In disgust he returned to his native Budapest, and eventually received an appointment at the University of Pest in 1855, instituting his hygienic procedures with good results, but with little recognition. This was true also of his great work "Die Aetiologie, der Begriff und die Prophylaxis des Kindbettfiebers" (The Etiology, Concept and Prophylaxis of Childbed Fever) published as a book in 1861. It was not well received and had poor foreign reviews. After this Semmelweis became gradually mentally ill, and in 1865 returned once again to Vienna where he died shortly afterwards. He was buried in Vienna, but his body was returned to his native Budapest in 1965.

Semmelweis is a tragic figure in medicine, but our debt to him is enormous, and he paved the way for the triumphs of Louis Pasteur.

The Semmelweis museum is the Hungarian peoples' tribute to their great son, and it is maintained by the state. The building was the Semmelweis family home. Ignác was born there, and is now buried there in a vault in the wall of the courtyard. The medical museum itself is extensive and one of the finest in the world. Its emphasis is of course on Semmelweis and his work, but in fact this is only a minor part of the total number of displays. In addition to the Semmelweis displays, there are exhibits on primitive medicine, Chinese, Greek, Roman and Islamic medicine, Renaissance medicine, the development and importance of the microscope, and the gradual advance of medicine in the 18th, 19th and 20th centuries, etc. There is also a magnificent medical historical library, archives, and portraits, etc. It is pleasant to record that the museum staff carries on an active program of research into the history of medicine. All in all a fine tribute to the memory of Ignác Semmelweis, and well worth the effort of a visit.

Chapter 9

HOLLAND

Holland, bordering on the North Sea and surrounded by powerful neighbors, has had a stormy history. Despite this the country has emerged today a small, independent and very prosperous nation. Over the centuries a high culture has evolved, particularly in art. From our point of view, and of the utmost importance, was their development of the magnifying lens and subsequently the microscope. The importance of the latter to modern biology and medicine can certainly not be overrated. The capital is The Hague (Den Haag), but Amsterdam is by far the largest, and in many ways the most important, city.

LEIDEN
Location - 15 kilometers northeast of The Hague and 35 kilometers southwest of Amsterdam.
Train - From The Hague or Amsterdam direct.
Road - Take the E10 from The Hague or Amsterdam and exit at Leiden.

Leiden is on what is referred to as the Old Rhine, and is connected by canals to Holland's two chief ports, Rotterdam and Amsterdam. It is an ancient town, criss-crossed with canals, and its industries are mainly weaving and bulb growing. As well as these industries it is an academic town containing the oldest and most important university in Holland. The University of Leiden was founded in 1575 as a reward to the inhabitants for their courageous defense against the Spaniards in 1574. It quickly established an international reputation, which it has maintained ever since.

Museum Boerhaave
(The National Museum for the History of Science)
University of Leiden
Steenstraat 1a
Leiden

Opening hours:
Monday - Saturday, 10.00 - 16.00
Sundays, 13.00 - 15.00
The times may however, vary with the seasons.
Small charge for admission.

This museum is near the railway station, and is part of the university. It is one of the top medical museums in the world. It is particularly famous for its collection of microscopes, and most of all for the fact that one can see here some of the original microscopes of Antoni van Leeuwenhoek (1632-1723). It is natural that he is somewhat of a Dutch hero.

Antoni van Leeuwenhoek was born in Delft into a middle class artisan family. He had an average education for the time, and in 1654 at the age of 22 set up as a shopkeeper. In the same year he married one Barbara de May, the daughter of an English cloth merchant. In 1660, at the age of 28, he gave up shopkeeping and entered the civil service. In one capacity or another he remained in this for the rest of his life. In 1666 his wife died, but five years later he was married again to Cornelia Swalmius, whom he outlived by 29 years.

Until Leeuwenhoek was nearly 40 we have no knowledge that he did anything which could be described as scientific. However, at that time he started, quite independently on his own, to grind simple lenses and construct these in the form of what we now call microscopes. He ground over 500 lenses during the rest of his life, and the magnifying power of these was truly remarkable. One of his lenses survives which has a magnifying power of 270! Having accomplished this remarkable feat, he set out to explore, in an ameteur's way, a whole new vista of biology which was opened up to him. In particular, he discovered what we now call microorganisms and understood their nature. He clearly saw and described a whole range of these, including bacteria, protozoa, rotifers and many more. Of equal importance, he was probably the first person to ever see sperm, and over a period of 40 years he accurately described these in arthropods, mollusks, fishes, amphibians, birds and mammals. He certainly knew they had a reproductive function, though it is questionable whether he understood the true nature of the fertilization of an egg by a sperm. Having seen all this, it is a pity, though perhaps inevitable for his time, that he had no concept of a cell.

Leeuwenhoek had no scientific training, never attended a university and had little idea of how to make his discoveries known. However, in 1676 he communicated some of his findings in a letter to the President of the Royal Society of London (see under London). In subsequent years he wrote over 100 letters to the Royal Society, and it is a great tribute to that body that they published these letters so that his observations and theories gradually became known. In his later years the importance of his work became widely recognized, and he was internationally honored. However, this in no way altered the nature of his simple and industrious life in Delft, where he died in 1723 at the age of 91.

Leeuwenhoek's biological contributions were great, but his microscopes were perhaps even greater. He would have been happy to know that over two centuries later, during World War II, and while under Nazi occupation, his native countrymen made the next major advance in microscopy by developing the "phase-contrast" microscope.

The displays at the Museum Boerhaave are extensive and include astronomy, medicine, biology and microscopy. The medical displays illustrate the development of such things as kidney machines, electrocardiograms, pharmacology, opthalmology, dentistry, treatments of many kinds and various instrumentations. All in all remarkable, and beautifully prepared exhibits.

The microscope collections are extensive. The "pièce de résistance" is a case containing two microscopes made and used by Antoni van Leeuwenhoek himself, one in brass with a magnification of 125, and one in silver with a magnification of 80. There is also an exact copy of one of Leeuwenhoek's microscopes with a magnification of 70. It is focused on the wing of a fly, and the visitor is permitted to look through this and see what Leeuwenhoek himself actually saw which was a great deal! Then there are displays of lens grinders, reading glasses going back to the 15th century, hand drawn illustrations of plants and animals done by early microscopists and the progression of these into the 19th and 20th centuries. There are also displays showing the complete progression of the microscope in the 18th, 19th and 20th centuries, with examples from the major manufacturers of different countries. Finally there is a large historical library with some priceless holdings going back as far as 1484.

We have certainly seen no finer biological and medical museum in any country, and with the help of its enthusiastic, knowledgeable and cooperative staff it is a pleasure to visit.

The Botanical Garden of the University of Leiden
Rapenburg 13
Leiden

Opening hours:
 Monday - Saturday, 9.00 - 16.00
 Sundays, 10.00 - 16.00
 The times may however, vary with the seasons.
 Small charge for admission.

This botanical garden was founded in 1587, which makes it one of the oldest in Europe, and it has played a large role in the development of medicine and horticulture in Holland.

In concluding this very short account of historical biology and medicine in Holland, we must point out that there are other places of interest which we have not yet been able to visit. However, some are mentioned in local guides, and we hope they will appear in later editions of this book.

Chapter 10

SWEDEN

Sweden, on the Baltic Sea, has a long tradition of excellence in a variety of human endeavors, and is today certainly one of the most socially advanced countries in the world. Time and time again, one is struck with the wealth of scientific ideas which originate in Sweden, and the Swedes continue to maintain incredibly high standards. We cannot refrain from pointing out that this state of affairs is at least in part due to the fact, that they have managed to keep their population small and more or less stable, and also to have stayed out of any major war for nearly 200 years!

LUND
Location - 625 kilometers southwest of Stockholm. 20 kilometers northeast of Malmö.
Train - From Stockholm and Malmö direct.
Road - From Stockholm take the E4 to the south, and at Helsingborg join the E6 to Lund and Malmö. From Malmö take route 15 to the north.

Lund was founded in 1020 by no less a person than King Canute (d. 1036), and subsequently became the religious, cultural, political and commercial center for much of Scandinavia. However, today Lund is a university town, which attracts our interest here, particularly because of its proximity to Malmö, which for many visitors will be their first point of contact with Sweden. A good way to get to Malmö is on the hydrofoil from Copenhagen, Denmark.

The University of Lund was founded in 1668. At first there was only a Faculty of Theology, but law and medicine soon followed. Today there are over 100 departments and about 20,000 students. Most of the present buildings date from the 19th century, the main building being in a park just off the Kyrkogatan. By application here, it is possible to get a walking tour of the university, but there is no regular schedule.

Of great interest is a lovely bronze statue of Carl Linnaeus in Petri Park, which is at the corner of Petri Kyrkog and Bredgatan.

Linnaeus studied medicine at Lund, but only for one year. In addition the visitor should not miss the University Apotek, a pharmacy dating from 1627. It is in the Kyrkogatan, and easily recognized by the pharmacist's symbol of a carved swan. Finally visitors will want to see the cathedral in the main square, with its huge medieval clock which tells the time, the date, the course of the sun and moon, etc. It is really quite an event when it chimes at noon!

STENBROHULT

Location - 475 kilometers southwest of Stockholm, and 150 kilometers northeast of Malmö.

Train - From Stockholm or Malmö to Växjö and then by bus or taxi to Stenbrohult.

Road - From Stockholm take the E4 south to Huskvarna, and then fork onto route 30 to Växjö. Then take route 23 towards Almhult, but before reaching Almhult turn off to Stenbrohult. From Malmö take route 23 towards Växjö, but shortly after Almhult turn off to Stenbrohult.

Stenbrohult is a small village southwest of Växjö, and it was here in 1707 that Carl Linnaeus (see under Uppsala) was born. His birthplace and other associations are well preserved.

Rashults Södergard
Stenbrohult

Opening hours:
Daily, 9.00 - 17.00
Small charge for admission.

This is an estate on the outskirts of Stenbrohult, which comprises several acres preserved as a park and contains the cabin where Linnaeus was born.

The whole estate is preserved much as it was in Linnaeus' day, and there are many interesting things to be learned about Swedish rural life in the early 18th century. This is true also of the Linnaean cabin, which was carefully restored in 1935. Inside the cabin, even the wallpaper is original from the 18th century, as is also the sparse furniture. Some of the furniture belonged to Linnaeus himself, and there are many cases containing some of his personal belongings and other mementos. There are also several original portraits of him done at various times in his life. The kitchen, with its open hearth and grey stone floor is original. There is also a loft containing costumes, furniture, utensils, etc. of the period. Just outside the house is an enclosed garden which is a replica of the one laid out by Linnaeus' father. Its accuracy to the original was confirmed by Carl's brother, who succeeded his father as vicar of Stenbrohult, and Carl himself visited the garden in 1731.

In Stenbrohult proper, the main associations with Linnaeus are in the grounds of the church, which border on a lake. Carl's father, Nicolaus, was the vicar here beginning in 1706. Just two years after Carl was born, the family moved to the new vicarage close to the church, and in these beautiful surroundings Carl spent many childhood years. Unfortunately the vicarage was destroyed by fire in 1720, and only the foundations survive. However, Linnaeus' close association with the area is commemorated by a very lovely statue of him as a young man.

Stenbrohult is an "out of the way" place, but well worth a visit by those interested in the history of botany.

UPPSALA
Location - 70 kilometers northwest of Stockhom.
Train - Direct from Stockholm.
Road - From Stockhom take the E4 to Uppsala.

Uppsala is a very ancient city, astride the river Fyris. It is the metropolitan see of the Swedish State Church, with a magnificent Gothic cathedral built between 1230-1435. The university was founded in 1477. Uppsala is of special interest to us, because it was here that Carl Linnaeus lived and worked for most of his life.

Carl Linnaeus (1707-1778) was born in Stenbrohult (see above), the son of the local parson. His father had a deep love of all things natural, but particularly of flowers and gardening, and he passed this love onto young Carl who embraced it for the rest of his life. He attended the cathedral school in nearby Växjö, intending at first to become a parson. However, his interest in botany was so strong that he soon abandoned theology. At that time the road to botany was through medicine and at 20 he entered the University of Lund to study this, and a year later transferred to Uppsala. In all it took him 8 years to get his medical degree, eventually from the Universtiy of Harderwijk in Holland in 1735. This was simply due to the fact that he was always botanizing instead of studying medicine!

While a student at Uppsala, Linnaeus immersed himself in botany, and developed the basis of what was to become his system of the classification of all living things. He was one of the first people to recognize plant sexuality, and he based his classification of these on their pistils and stamens. At the same time he developed the concept of what we now call the binomial nomenclature, which is the basis of all modern classification. It is important to note that Linnaeus had no thought of organic evolution as we know it today, but his system of classification has been adopted for the naming of plants and animals in their evolutionary relationships.

In 1735 Linnaeus left Uppsala and traveled extensively in France, Holland and England. In the same year at the early age of 28, his monumental work "Systema Naturae" (The System of Nature) was published in Leiden, Holland. Although he had published many works on botany before, this quickly established him as the leading botanist of the world. In 1738 he returned to Sweden, married Elizabeth Moraea, and for a time set up medical practice in Stockhom, before being appointed professor of medicine in Uppsala. However, things were arranged so that he could devote most of his time to botany. For the rest of his life, Linnaeus remained at the University of Uppsala studying and writing about botany. His output, particularly on the flora of Sweden, was enormous, but it may safely be said that his reputation as the foremost botanist of all time rests on the new concepts of classification which he put forth in his "Systema Naturae." He died in Uppsala in 1778, and is buried in the catheral.

Linnémuseet
Svartbäcksgatan 27
Uppsala

Opening hours:
Museum, Tuesday - Sunday 13.00 - 16.00
Garden, Tuesday - Sunday 9.00 - dusk.
Both closed Mondays.
Small charge for admission.

This is the Linnaen museum and garden in Uppsala. The garden dates from 1635, and was the original botanic garden of the university. When Linnaeus came to Uppsala as a professor of medicine in 1741 he took over responsibility for the garden, and lived in the house which went with the position. Under Linnaeus' direction, the gardens were greatly improved and laid out in baroque style. Of great interest also is the fact that he arranged the plants according to his newly developed sexual system. Today we would call this a taxonomic garden, and this is certainly the oldest such garden in the world. After Linnaeus' death the garden fell into decay, but fortunately he left an exact description of it in his Hortus Uppsaliensis (1745), and when the garden was restored in 1917 by the Swedish Linnaen Society, Linnaeus' original plan was faithfully followed. Thus the visitor today can see and walk in this same garden which Linnaeus himself laid out.

The adjoining house, in which Linnaeus lived for many years is now the Linnaen Museum. When Linnaeus died in 1778, almost all of his huge collections of plants and animals, as well as his library, letters and manuscripts, were sold at public auction in Stockholm. The highest bidder was a young wealthy English medical student, James Edward Smith, and in due course he shipped the collections to London where they became the basis of the Linnaen Society of London (see under London). However, Linnaeus' household effects remained in the hands of his family, and were returned to the house in 1935 when it was restored as a museum. It is in fact exceptionally well stocked, and everything in it belonged either to Carl Linnaeus himself or his family. There is no doubt it is much the same as Linnaeus would have known it. There is a wealth of furniture, clothes, utensils, etc., also many of Linnaeus' instruments, notebook, published books, portraits of him, etc., all beautifully kept and displayed. Finally there is a nice bronze statue of him in the courtyard entrance to the museum.

Carolina Rediviva
Drottninggatan and Dag Hammarskjölds Vag
Uppsala

Opening hours:
> Daily, but times vary considerably.
> No charge for admission.

This is the University Library, and the largest library in Sweden.

Of great interest to us, however, is the Linnaen collection housed in a special room. It is not normally open to the public, but permission to see it can be requested from the librarian. It is without doubt the most extensive Linnaen collection in the world, but unfortunately without Linnaeus' own library (see under London).

In public areas of the library are displays, under glass, of some priceless old books and maps. One of these is the Codex Argenteus or Silver Bible. It was probably written in Ravenna, Italy about 500 A.D. It is composed of purple vellum with silver and gold letters. A most remarkable sight!

Gustavianum
Uppsala

Opening hours:
> Monday - Friday, 8.00 - 16.00
> No charge for admission.

This is a unique anatomy theatre located in the main square of Uppsala just behind the cathedral. It was built in 1663, and was a copy of the anatomy theatre in Padua, Italy (see under Italy) of the previous century. It was a gift to the University of Uppsala from one of its professors, Olof Rudbeck (1630-1702), who, in 1650 when only 19 years old, discovered the lymph system--no mean achievement! The theatre is all hand carved wood, very lovely, and the second oldest in the world.

Domkyrkan
Uppsala

Opening hours:
> Variable - must inquire locally.
> This is an active church.

The Cathedral of Uppsala, located in the center of the city, took some 200 years to build, and was completed in 1435. It is the largest church in Scandinavia. From our point of view, however, all biologically minded visitors will want to visit it to see the tomb of Carl Linnaeus.

Linnaeus' Hammarby
Uppsala

Opening hours:
> Buildings, daily 12.00 - 16.00
> Grounds, daily 8.00 - dusk.
> Small charge for admission.

This is the former country house and farm of Linnaeus. It is about 10 kilometers south of Uppsala and can be reached by a local, but infrequent, bus from the station. It is best however, to take a taxi if possible. Linnaeus purchased the farm in 1758, and it remained in family hands until 1879 when it was purchased by the state as a permanent memorial to Linnaeus. The main building was Linnaeus' house where he lived with his family. It is quite spacious and well maintained much as it was when Linnaeus lived there. It is well stocked with furniture, portraits, books, etc., and in some rooms the walls are papered with prints of his plant illustrations and drawings. The outside of the building has been boarded over, which is a pity, but apparently necessary to preserve the original logs.

The grounds and adjoining woods are a joy to wander in, particulary in spring. Here Linnaeus "cultivated his garden" and introduced so many new species of plants. There is indeed little doubt that the columbines and lilies, which flourish in the woods, are direct descendants of those which Linnaeus planted himself. It is a truly thrilling experience to spend a few hours at this beautiful place and celebrate the memory of the world's greatest botanist. It is also a fitting and pleasant place to end our account of Sweden.

Chapter 11

UNITED STATES OF AMERICA

The biological and medical history of the United States must be viewed in the overall context of its general history. This, as compared to the countries we have already considered, is relatively short, and in addition much of this has been primarily concerned with frontier and quick developmental problems, rather than with science. Indeed we think it reasonably accurate to say that science in the United States did not come into its own until World War II, but with this it quickly became one of the leading scientific countries of the world. There is another pertinent factor however, which is that as a nation it is not very good at preserving its cultural heritage, the regrettable tendency being to bulldoze everything under and start again. In addition it is a large country, expensive to get around in, and thus we have not yet been able to visit and describe some of the places we would have liked to. All this having been said, there are some things of historical interest and importance in biology and medicine with which to tempt the reader. Since almost everything we will refer to is in a large city, we do not think it necessary to indicate their location or how to get to them.

BOSTON

Boston, Massachusetts, is one of the oldest cities in the U.S.A., and has played a major role in the cultural development of the country, not the least aspect of which has been its role in scientific development. This has largely been based in and around Harvard University, which is the oldest institution of learning in the United States. It was founded in 1636, and at first conferred only arts degrees, but as early as 1782 it had a medical school. This, together with the accompanying biological and physical sciences has generally prospered, and today Harvard is one of the great universities of the world. It was in close association with the Harvard Medical Faculty, that the first introduction of surgical anaesthesia in medicine took place in 1846. A major milestone in the history of medicine.

Massachusetts General Hospital
Cambridge and North Grove Streets
Boston, Massachusetts

Opening hours:
>Normal business hours.
>This is an active hospital.

The Massachusetts General Hospital is the oldest in Boston, with origins going back to the early 19th century, and is today a vast complex of buildings. Its world-wide fame is due to many discoveries and events which have taken place there, but none compares in importance with the first effective use of surgical anaesthesia which was administered there on October 16, 1846.

There is considerable doubt as to who was actually the first person to use anaesthesia effectively, in the sense of suppressing pain, particularly during surgery. Thus a short account here of this history is pertinent, and will give the reader more perspective.

It has been pointed out elsewhere (see under London and Edinburgh, Britain) that operations prior to anaesthesia can only be described as "nightmares," and were usually confined to amputations or some form of superficial surgery. Nevertheless pain suppressing drugs have been used throughout recorded history, heroin and alcohol are two common examples, and the art of hypnotism has also been used for centuries. However, towards the end of the 18th century chemistry was far enough advanced that new gases were becoming available which had extraordinary properties. One of these was nitrous oxide (commonly called laughing gas) and the famous English chemist, Sir Humphry Davy (1778-1829) experimented with this as early as 1799. He tried it out on himself, realized it produced insensibility to pain, and suggested that it should be used during operations. Nothing seems to have come of this, probably because the social and medical "climate" was still not ripe for such a novel idea.

During the early part of the 19th century other gases were produced, and one of these was sulphuric ether. This also produced insensibility to pain, and it became popular amongst the socially elite, particularly in the United States, in the form of "ether frolics." These were essentially "avant-garde" parties during which the participants sniffed varying amounts of ether. At one of these, the imagination of a young surgeon from Georgia was aroused by the fact that when a person under the influence of ether was injured he did not seem to feel any pain. The surgeon's name was Crawford

Williamson Long (1815-1878), and he immediately realized the potential of ether. On March 30, 1841, he tried it out successfully on one of his patients during the removal of a tumor from the neck. We know very little about Long. He was born in Danielsville, Georgia in 1815, received his early education in Athens, Georgia, studied medicine and received his degree from the University of Pennsylvania in 1839. After graduation he worked for a while in various New York hospitals, but soon went back to Georgia where he became a successful physician. He died in Athens in 1878.

Shortly after Crawford Long first used ether as an anaesthetic, a young dentist named Horace Wells (1815-1848) from Hartford, Vermont, used nitrous oxide on himself while an assistant painlessly extracted one of his teeth. This was in 1844, and Wells subsequently used nitrous oxide on many of his patients. Wells was thoroughly convinced of the effectiveness of nitrous oxide, and in 1844 he persuaded a Dr. John Collins Warren of the Harvard Medical School to let him demonstrate his discovery during the extraction of a tooth at the Massachusetts General Hospital. Unfortunately, the demonstration failed, as the patient experienced severe pain, and Wells was laughed out of the hospital. Thereafter Wells was a tragic figure. He became addicted to chloroform, with which he also experimented, his mind failed, and in 1848 at the early age of 33 he committed suicide, while in a New York jail.

Wells at one time had a dental partner by the name of William Thomas Morton (1819-1868). He was born in Charlton, Massachusetts, and studied dentistry in Baltimore. He was also a medical student at Harvard, but left before receiving his degree. While practicing dentistry in Boston he got to know a chemist by the name of Charles T. Jackson, who gave him some ether and suggested its use as an anaesthetic. Morton successfully used ether on a patient in September 1846, and a few weeks later persuaded Dr. Warren, the Harvard surgeon, to let him give, like Wells before him, a public demonstration of this at the Massachusetts General Hospital. This was done on October 16, 1846. There are several fragmentary and differing accounts of this great event. The name of the patient was Gilbert Abbott, and he was to have a tumor removed from his neck. Morton was late for the operation -- not a good beginning!-- but in due course he arrived and administered the ether by mouth from his primitive inhalator. Dr. Warren then proceeded with the operation, which lasted about three minutes, during which the patient did not move nor indicate any signs of pain. When it was over and the patient aroused, Dr. Warren asked him if he had felt anything, to which he replied "I thought I felt someone scratching at my neck" upon which Warren turned to his audience and said, "Gentlemen, this is no humbug. We have seen something today that will go around the whole world!" Warren's words proved to be correct, even though it took a considerable time to improve the techniques of administration of the drug. But effective anaesthesia was henceforth on its way as a medical aid, and one of the greatest blessings to humans. The introduction of anaesthesia ranks with antisepsis as a major medical advance, and both of them were prerequisite to the development of modern surgery.

Unfortunately the story of the discovery of anaesthesia does not have a happy ending. After Morton's demonstration in the Massachusetts General Hospital the news spread rapidly, but there ensued a bitter controversy between Morton, Jackson, Wells and Long as to priority. Jackson, Wells and Long wanted nothing from their discovery except to benefit mankind. The same cannot be said of Morton, who generally does not seem to have been a likeable character. He tried for the rest of his life to patent anaesthesia and extract a royalty for every anaesthetic given. However he was unsuccessful in this, neglected his practice, and died in poverty in New York in 1868.

The Ether Dome
Bullfinch Building

The scene where the famous first operation using anaesthesia took place is in the Ether Dome of the Bullfinch Building. The dome can actually be seen on top of the building from the outside, but is best seen from the inside. Permission for this must be obtained from the hospital administration, but is normally granted if the room is not in use. The Ether Dome was originally the operating amphitheatre of the hospital and was used as such from 1821-1867. It has undergone several alterations since then, and is now used as a demonstration and lecture room. Nevertheless, it was here that anaesthesia became a meaningful reality, a fact commemorated by a large plaque on the main wall of the amphitheatre. It reads as follows:

ON OCTOBER 16, 1846 IN THIS ROOM THEN THE OPERATING
THEATRE OF THE HOSPITAL
WAS GIVEN THE FIRST PUBLIC DEMOSTRATION OF
ANAESTHESIA TO THE EXTENT OF

PRODUCING INSENSIBILITY TO PAIN DURING A SERIOUS
SURGICAL OPERATION. SULPHURIC ETHER WAS
ADMINISTERED BY WILLIAM THOMAS GREEN MORTON
A BOSTON DENTIST
THE PATIENT WAS GILBERT ABBOTT
THE OPERATION WAS THE REMOVAL OF A TUMOR UNDER THE
JAW THE SURGEON WAS JOHN COLLINS WARREN
THE PATIENT DECLARED THAT HE HAD FELT NO PAIN DURING
THE OPERATION AND WAS DISCHARGED WELL DECEMBER 7
KNOWLEDGE OF THIS DISCOVERY SPREAD FROM THIS ROOM
THROUGHOUT THE CIVILIZED WORLD
AND A NEW ERA FOR SURGERY BEGAN

It is a truly emotionally rewarding experience to stand in this room and realize the great event which took place here. In the room there are also displays of various early types of apparatus for the administration of anaesthetics.

As pointed out previously, Morton administered his anaesthetic by mouth from a glove-like glass inhalator. The original of this survives, but is so valuable that it is kept in the hospital vault and is not available for viewing. However, an exact replica of it has been made, and this is displayed in the main corridor of the ground floor of the Bullfinch Building. There are other fascinating display cases here as well. The visitor cannot help but be impressed with the long way we have come since the introduction of anaesthesia in 1846. There are many other interesting places in Boston, which are of interest in the history of biology and medicine, but none approaches in importance the one we have described.

CLEVELAND

The Howard Dittrick Museum of Historical Medicine
11000 Euclid Avenue
Cleveland, Ohio

Opening hours:
>   Monday - Friday, 10.00 - 17.00
>   Sundays, 13.00 - 17.00
>   Small charge for admission.

Our knowledge of this museum, founded in 1926, is secondhand, for we have not been able to visit it. However, it is said to have some fine collections and displays in the history of medicine.

MACKINAC ISLAND
Michigan

This is an island in Lake Huron at its northwestern tip, just where it joins Lake Michigan. It was here on June 6, 1822 that an accident occurred which gave an opportunity to an American army doctor to make some very important discoveries in the field of gastric physiology. The doctor's name was William Beaumont (1785-1853) and he made full use of the opportunity. This event is commemorated here. The island can only be reached by ferry (no cars) from either Mackinaw City or St. Ignace.

William Beaumont was born in Lebanon, Connecticut, the son of a farmer. He did not wish to become a farmer himself, left home as a young man, and for about three years he taught in primary schools, but soon became a doctor's apprentice and received a license in 1812 to practice in Vermont. This was the year war broke out between Britain and the United States, and Beaumont quickly joined the army as a surgeon. He served in a variety of places, but in 1822 he was ordered to Fort Mackinac, and on June 6th the now famous accident occurred. -- A French Canadian trapper by the name of Alexis St. Martin, received a massive wound in his left side from a musket. Both the stomach and one lung were severely damaged. He was quickly put under the care of Beaumont, who did what he could for him, but he did not expect the trapper to live. However, in one of those rare instances where "nature simply takes a hand," Alexis St. Martin did live, and as the wound healed a gastric fistula developed between the abdominal surface and the interior of the stomach. The word fistula is derived from the latin, meaning "pipe," and this accurately described the situation, for through the abdominal opening the surgeon had direct access to a living functional stomach. Beaumont quickly realized that here was a golden opportunity to carry out investigations into digestion in a living person, and from 1825-1833 he used Alexis St. Martin as the subject of a variety of experiments. Beaumont's knowledge of chemistry was very limited, but he sought good advice, and quickly established the presence of free hydrochloric acid in the stomach and also the contractions of the stomach muscles. These were merely preliminary observations. He went on to show that gastric

211

juice secretion, and thus digestion, were greatly influenced by psychic factors, that the juice was not found in the stomach in the absence of food, and that water passed rapidly out of the stomach into the duodenum. He also studied the effects on gastric secretion of various foods, including coffee, tea and alcohol.

Beaumont's experiments ended in 1833 with the publication of his great work "Experiments and Observations of the Gastric Juice and the Physiology of Digestion." It is one of the great works of experimental medicine and laid the foundations of the science of digestive physiology.

Beaumont left the army in 1839 and went into private practice. All accounts indicate he was good at this, and was a popular physician. He died in 1853 as a result of an accidental fall.

The William Beaumont Memorial Building
Mackinac Island
Mackinac Island State Park Commission
Lansing, Michigan

Opening hours:
> May 15th - October 20th only.
> Daily, 9.00 - 17.00
> These times may change, so be sure to check with the park headquarters.

Regrettably, we have not been to this memorial, but what follows comes directly form the superintendent of the State Park.

The Beaumont Memorial on Mackinac Island was a gift to the park by the Michigan State Medical Society. It consists of the building, formerly the American Fur Company's retail store, where Alexis St. Martin was accidentally shot. It has been completely restored. On the gound floor there are two rooms, the first furnished with French-Canadian furniture of the period, and the second with Beaumont's furniture. There is also the Dean Cornwell painting of William Beaumont and Alexis St. Martin. On the second floor there is a medical history museum, which includes some of Beaumont's instruments. Also four full scale dioramas depicting phases of the physician's life and experiments. Finally at Fort Mackinac itself, there is a monument to Beaumont and in the Fort Museum there is a Beaumont exhibit.

NEW YORK

New York, N.Y. is a vast metropolitan complex, one of the largest in the world. Its origins go back to Dutch colonization in 1626, when the area was called New Amsterdam. Control passed to the British in 1664 when it was renamed New York, and at the time of the revolution it became one of the principle centers in the newly founded United States. Since then it has always played a major role in the development of the country, and in recent times a few famous institutions dedicated to the study of biology and medicine have been established there, and have played important roles.

American Museum of Natural History
Central Park West at 79th Street
New York, N.Y.

Opening hours:
   Monday, Tuesday, Thursday and Friday, 10.00 - 16.45
   Wednesdays, 10.00 - 21.00
   Saturdays, Sundays and holidays, 10.00 - 17.00
   Small charge for admission.

The American Museum of Natural History is today one of the foremost in the world, and has played a very important role in the progress of all modern biology.

The museum was founded in 1869 for the purpose of advancing various branches of natural knowledge. It was founded a private institution and has remained so ever since, but is associated with the City University of New York and Columbia University, so that students from these universities can study at the museum. Most of the research work of the museum is not normally seen by the public, and includes such areas as animal behavior, anthropology, entomology, herpetology, ichthyology, invertebrates, mammalogy, ornithology and vertebrate paleontology. Over many years the staff of the museum have played important roles in advancing our knowledge of these areas.

The displays on view for the public are extensive. All the major groups of animals, both living and in fossil form, are represented, and there are exhibits of rocks and minerals as well. The museum also carries on active educational programs in the form of lectures, field trips, etc., and publishes a wide range of journals and magazines. Perhaps above all however, is their superb library. It is principally devoted to natural history with some priceless rare books in the field, and is probably the best such library in North America. It is not open for use by the public except by permission of the librarian. However, visitors can ask permission to see it. Sometimes there are special displays of their rare books.

The American Museum of Natural History has something to offer everyone interested in the history of biology, and indeed a lot more.

New York Academy of Medicine
2 East 103rd Steet
New York, N.Y.

Opening hours:
Normal business hours.
No charge for admission.

The New York Academy of Medicine was founded in 1847, for the purpose of promoting the science and art of medicine, the promotion of public health and medical education, and the maintenance of a library of medicine. It is a pleasure to record that through the years it has remained true to these founding functions, and it has played a very important role in the successes of modern medicine, particularly in the United States.

Most of the work of the Academy is in the promotion of medicine and not directly visible, but this is not the case for their library which is certainly one of the best medical libraries in North America. There are over 500,000 volumes, with special collections, very rare and old medical books, as well as some important original medical manuscripts. The library can be used by qualified persons with the permission of the librarian, and visitors can request to see various aspects of it. This library is priceless and continues to play an important role in the advance of medicine.

PHILADELPHIA

Philadelphia, Pennsylvania, is one of the most historic cities in the United States. It was founded by William Penn in 1682 as a city in which people of all races and religions might live together without persecution. Benjamin Franklin was closely associated with the city, and he was responsible for the founding there of many libraries and educational institutions. Philadelphia was a major focus of revolutionary activity in the latter part of the 18th century. It was here that the Constitution of the United States was drawn up, independence proclaimed, and Philadelphia subsequently became the first capital of the new country. From our point of view however, Philadelphia has also been a major center for the study and progress of medicine.

Pennsylvania Hospital
Eighth and Spruce Streets
Philadelphia, PA

Opening hours:
     Normal business hours.
     This is an active hospital.

This was the nation's first voluntary hospital, and was founded by Dr. Thomas Bond and Benjamin Franklin in 1751. Its purpose was solely for the relief of the "sick and the miserable," a fact commemorated in the inscription on the cornerstone of the Pine Building which was laid in 1755. The Pine Building still survives, and contains a wealth of medical history. This building is still in active use, but guided tours can be arranged by appointment through the administration. Interesting literature is available.

Originally many of the patients were insane, and the Pine Building was designed with a moat, which can still be seen. It was a popular pastime on Sundays for the "sane" to go to the hospital to marvel at the "insane," and the purpose of the moat was as a mutual barrier between the two! In the main lobby is a huge painting by Benjamin West of "Christ Healing the Sick," in which most of the major known ailments of the time were depicted. In addition there are fine portraits of early American doctors. -- Perhaps of greatest interest is the old operating amphitheatre located in the roof of the building with a glass dome. This is the oldest surviving operating theatre in the world and dates from 1804. Operating theatres of this period were always placed in the roof for two reasons. First to get the maximum amount of light, and secondly to be as isolated as possible, so that the screams of patients (there were no anaesthetics) could not be heard elsewhere. Operating days were really quite an occasion. They were advertised in advance, and anybody could buy tickets to get in. The doctors had no idea of cleanliness, and even sharpened their knives on the soles of their boots. This theatre saw the introduction of anaesthetics, and was in use for operations until 1868, but since then has undergone several alterations. Nevertheless it is still the original room and the visitor may ponder some of the terrible agonies suffered by patients here, and be thankful that this is no longer necessary. Elsewhere in the building are many other artifacts of medical history, including the chains used as manacles to restrain the patients.

At this hospital, there is also one of the finest historical medical libraries in the world, with holdings going back to the 15th century. It can only be used by permission of the librarian, but visitors may ask to see it.

Finally we must mention a fine statue of William Penn in the courtyard of the Pine Building, and from this courtyard the dome of the old operating amphitheatre can also be seen.

The College of Physicians of Philadelphia
19 South 22nd Street
Philadelphia, PA

Opening hours:
Monday - Friday only, 10.00 -17.00
No charge for admission.

This College of Physicians was founded in 1787 and organized in much the same way as its British counterpart. Its purpose was to advance the science and art of medicine, and it still carries on in this tradition. There are three things here which are of great historical interest, and can be seen by visitors with the permission of the secretary.

The first of the three things to see is the Mutter Medical Museum, which was patterned after the famous Hunterian Museum in the Royal College of Surgeons in London (see under London). The extensive displays in this museum basically illustrate the development of the life sciences. There is a wealth of old instruments (going back to Roman times), anatomical and pathological specimens, etc., all beautifully cared for. It is also of great interest architecturally, with its high balcony surrounding the main floor.

The other two things to see are the superb historical medical library, and the Herb Garden, newly restored. Also throughout the building are striking portraits of early American doctors.

WASHINGTON

Washington, D.C. was made the capital of the United States by an Act of Congress in 1790, and the government was transferred there from Philadelphia in 1800. It was laid out in "the grand style," and in many ways is one of the most impressive cities in the country. Apart from government, there are fortunately many major cultural institutions and we will describe some of these which are important in the history of biology and medicine.

National Museum of History and Technology
14th Street and Constitution Avenue, N.W.
Washington, D.C.

Opening hours:
Daily, 10.00 - 17.30
No charge for admission.

This is a branch of the Smithsonian Institution, a federally-chartered corporaton. It carries on a great variety of scientific investigations, and has been assigned many major responsibilities by the government. The origin of the Smithsonian is of great interest. In 1826, an Englishman named James Smithson bequeathed £100,000 to the United States government to found an institution in Washington for "the increase and diffusion of knowledge among men," and the Smithsonian Institution has certainly lived up to that charge. It has become one of the great scientific institutions of the world, though its activities are by no means confined to science.

The National Museum of History and Technology is one of three adjacent museums on Constitution Avenue, the other two being the Museum of Natural History and the National Gallery of Art. What is of such significance, is that here are extensive displays in the history of biology, medicine and dentistry, and they are certainly the best in the United States. They tend to be oriented to American history in these fields, but have an international flavor as well. In describing these we can do no better than list some of the superbly designed displays:

1. Early Pharmacy
2. A United States Drugstore of 1890
3. The Development of Antibiotics
4. Early Dentistry
5. Reconstruction of dental offices and equipment of 1885 and 1900

6. A variety of historical dental instruments, and dentures worn by George Washington.
7. The Development of X-rays
8. Electricity and Medicine
9. Historical Optometry
10. The historical development of stethoscopes, opthalmoscopes, etc.
11. History of Bacteriological Research
12. History of Microscopes
13. Early surgery
14. Surgical Milestones
15. History of Anaesthesia
16. Development of Electrocardiographs
17. Rehabilitation Medicine
18. Modern Surgery

This is only a partial list, and the visitor interested in such history may spend many productive hours learning from these excellent exhibits.

The Library of Congress
10 First Street S.E.
Washington, D.C.

Opening hours:
Daily, 9.00 - 18.00
There is a 45 minute tour of the library, which leaves the main entrance rotunda, every hour on the hour, from 9.00 - 16.00 weekdays only.
No charge for admission.

This is popularly described as "The Nation's Library," and is today probably the largest library in the world. Its holdings cover every field of human knowledge. It administers the copyright system in the United States and is the depository of all copyright books in this country.

It was founded by an act of Congress in 1800, and its early holdings were primarily in the area of parliamentary government. During the War of 1812, the Capitol was burnt in 1814 and with it went the library. However the following year Congress purchased the private library of former President Thomas Jefferson (1743-1826) and this formed the nucleus from which the present library

218

has grown. Its holdings are remarkably extensive -- "from Egyptian papyrus to micorfilm."

The Library of Congress in not a library for everday use, but rather a reference library for scholars and other libraries, but there are very interesting rooms with special exhibits. A visit to this magnificent library which has played such a major role in our whole culture is a truly thrilling experience.

The National Library of Medicine
8600 Rockville Pike
Bethesda, Maryland

Before leaving Washington we just want to mention the National Library of Medicine in nearby Bethesda. Founded in 1836, it is the foremost Library of Medicine in the United States. It is with some regret that we cannot describe it from first-hand experience, as we have not been there. However, there can be no question that it is an important place for those interested in the history of medicine.

WILLIAMSBURG

Williamsburg, Virginia was one of the original settlements of the early colonists from England, and became the first capital of Virginia. But by the early 20th century it had faded into just a small provincial town, and might have remained that way if it had not been for the farsightedness and generosity of John D. Rockefeller Jr., who has restored the town to an approximation of what it was like in colonial times during the 17th and 18th centuries. It is a remarkable piece of work, and of extreme interest. There is something of historical value for everyone at Colonial Williamsburg, including those concerned with the history of medicine.

The Apothecary Shop
Duke of Gloucester Street
Williamsburg, VA

Opening hours:
> Daily, 10.00 - 17.00, but there are variations depending on the season. There is a considerable charge for admission to the entire complex of Colonial Williamsburg.

The Apothecary Shop is a restoration built on its original foundations as it existed from 1760-1780.

In a previous chapter (see Heidelburg, Germany) we have explained the importance of the apothecary in the development of medicine, and the drugs it employs, and here in this shop is a fine display of the "wares" of an 18th century apothecary, with a curator very willing to explain it all and demonstrate some of the techniques. The shop is divided into two parts, front and back. In the front is the apothecary's domain, but in an office at the back is a fine collection of 18th century medical instruments. These actually belonged to Dr. John Minson Galt (1744-1808), who practiced in Williamsburg during the latter half of the 18th century. They are rather grim, and include cases of instruments designed for removing stones, amputations of limbs, and trephining--a process of boring into the skull, which was supposed to "relieve pressure," and this was done without any anaesthetic! All in all a visit to this Apothecary Shop leaves one with the impression that modern times have some advantages!

Chapter 12

CANADA

Visitors to Canada would do well to understand that it is a bilingual country, based on the fact that its origins go back to a struggle for possession between the French and British. That struggle was finally settled in 1759 with a British victory over the French on the Plains of Abraham, near modern Quebec City. However, the British were, considering the times, tolerant rulers, and many French settlers remained in the country and have subsequently played a major role in its history. Modern Canada was established in 1867 by the British North America Act. With it came a constitution, though it is not an imitation of the United States constitution, but rather the British constitution federalized, which includes many unwritten conventions. Today Canada is a modern "western country," with a relatively small population for its vast territorial size. The capital city is Ottawa.

Until very recent times, Canadian science and medicine were far more closely integrated with those of Britain, but with the huge expansion of these fields in the United States from World War II onwards, Canadian science and medicine have inevitably accommodated to this fact. Nevertheless they have their own independent traditions, and are likely to cling to them.

TORONTO

Toronto, Ontario, is the number two city in Canada, and along with Montreal, can certainly be considered the home of Canadian medicine. It was here in 1921 that a truly great medical event took place, namely, the demonstration of the antidiabetic properties of insulin, and its subsequent use in therapy. It was the first major therapeutic application of a hormone. In its day it was senstational with its almost miraculous results. It should be made clear that there are several kinds of diabetes, but the one which has been of such importance in human history is diabetes mellitus (from the Latin, and it literally means honey diabetes). It is a chronic form of diabetes, characterized by an excess of sugar in the blood and urine, together with hunger, thirst, gradual loss of weight and other side effects commonly leading to death. It has plagued mankind throughout recorded history, and it is only since 1921 that it has been brought under control (there is still no cure) by the therapeutic use of insulin. Indeed many millions of diabetics owe their lives, and their ability to live a more or less satisfactory existence, to this discovery. Traditionally the credit for the discovery has always gone to Frederick Banting (1891-1941), and Charles Best (1899-1978), but that is certainly a simplification of the realities, if not an outright distortion, and unfortunately instead of giving full credit to all those responsible, "nationalism" reared its ugly head with the inevitable misrepresentation. The initial work was indeed carried out by Banting and Best, but this was done in the laboratory of Professor John James Macleod, a Scotsman, under his guidance and with the input of his vast experience and knowledge. In addition the biochemist J.B. Collip played a crucial role in purifying the insulin. However, there was one organization that was not intimidated by the "propaganda," and that was the Nobel Committee in Sweden. For when they awarded the Nobel Prize in 1923, they awarded it to Macleod and Banting, albeit under a storm of protest. They knew what they were doing--but in Toronto it is still Banting and Best who are the heroes!

Frederick Banting was born in Alliston, Ontario, and grew up on the family farm. He went to local schools, and in due course entered the University of Toronto to study theology, but soon transferred to medicine, receiving a M.B. degree in 1916. At this time World War I was at its height, and Banting was soon in the Canadian Army. He was wounded and decorated, but at the end of the war returned to the University of Toronto to study for his M.D. degree. He was briefly associated with the University of Western Ontario in London, but in the spring of 1921 returned to the University of Toronto to undertake research with Charles Best on diabetes, and this work was to be crowned with success. A year later Banting and Best were world famous, and their technique of treating diabetes with insulin is still in use today. Banting was awarded the Nobel Prize in 1923, and honors from all over the world poured in upon him. The same year he became Director of Medical Research at the University of Toronto, and the following year was knighted. He himself pursued an active research career, mainly in the fields of cancer and heart disease. In 1939 World War II started, and Banting was again quickly in the Canadian Army Medical Corps. This ended in tragedy, for in 1941 he was killed in an air crash in Newfoundland while on his way to England. His body was recovered, and now rests in Mount Pleasant Cemetery in Toronto.

Charles Best was born in West Pembroke, Maine, of Canadian parents, who soon afterwards moved back to Canada and eventually to Toronto. Best received his education in Toronto, which was interrupted by service in World War I. In 1921 he received a B.A. degree in physiology and biochemistry from the University of Toronto. It was that summer, while he was just 22, that he worked with Banting on the diabetes problem. Despite his almost immediate fame, he returned to the University of Toronto as a student, receiving his M.D. degree in 1925, and until his retirement was actively engaged in medical research. In 1929 he became head of the university's Department of Physiology, and in 1941 head of the newly established Banting and Best Department of Medical Research. His name is closely associated with the development of such new drugs as histamine, heparin, choline and others. He died in Toronto in 1978 and is buried in Mount Pleasant Cemetery.

The Charles H. Best Institute
112 College Street
Toronto

Opening hours:
Normal business hours.
No charge for admission.
This is a working institute of medical research.

The Old Medical Sciences Building where Banting and Best worked no longer survives. In place of it is a huge medical complex on the west side of Queen's Park. Outside this complex is a large brass plaque which commemorates the event which took place there. However, just across Queen's Park on College Street, is the Charles H. Best Institute. This was opened in 1953 in honor of the great work of Charles Best and Sir Frederick Banting. It is primarily devoted to medical research, but visitors are welcome on the ground floor where there are many portraits etc. of famous doctors, including Best himself. In addition they have some of the original equipment, including Best's colorimeter, which he and Banting used in the summer of 1921. It is fascinating to see how primitive, by modern standards, this equipment was, yet they achieved so much. The equipment, documents, photographs, etc. may be seen by application to the business office of the institute. It is well worth the effort involved.

The Thomas Fisher Rare Book Library
120 St. George Street
Toronto

Opening hours:
October - April, Monday - Saturday 9.00 - 17.00
May - September, Monday - Friday 9.00 - 17.00
Closed on Sundays and all public holidays.
No charge for admission.

This is under the direction of the main library of the University of Toronto, but is a seperate building (opened 1973) devoted to rare books and special collections. There is also a display area on the second floor, where there are regularly changing exhibitions. There are particularly fine collections in English literature, Italian Renaissance literature and for our particluar purposes, incredible collections of science and medicine from the Renaissance to the 20th century. Included amongst these is perhaps the finest Darwinian collection outside the Cambridge University Library in England (see under Cambridge, England). We cannot recommend this superb historical library too strongly.

The William Boyd Library and Medical Museum
The Toronto Academy of Medicine
288 Bloor Street West,
Toronto

Opening hours:
Monday - Friday only, 9.30 - 16.00
No charge for admission.

This institution has a small but excellent medical historical library, and a limited but very good medical museum.

The Ontario Science Center
770 Don Mills Road (at Eglinton)
Toronto

Opening hours:
> Daily, 10.00 - 18.00
> Small charge for admission.

This is an enormous science and technology museum. Many years in the building, it was opened in 1964 in celebration of the 100th year of the founding of the Province of Ontario.

The museum's main function is education in a broad field of subjects, and the excellent displays range from aeronautics and astronomy to medicine and natural history. It is not necessary to mention them all here, suffice it to say there are many, and we can hardly overstress the size of the museum, it is enormous. Of particular interest to us is a complete natural size replica of the laboratory used by Banting and Best in 1921. It is most impressive. Some years before his death we had an interview with Dr. Charles Best and we asked him if indeed it was an accurate copy of the original. "Yes" he replied, "as I recall things it is very accurate, with the one exception that it is much cleaner than the original!"

VANCOUVER

Vancouver, British Columbia, is the principle city of Canada on the west coast, and is fast becoming a major cultural and scientific center.

The Charles Woodward Memorial room
Woodward Biomedical Library
University of British Columbia
Vancouver, B.C.

Opening hours:
> Monday - Friday only, 9.00 - 17.00
> No charge for admission.
> This is open to the public, but permission to use it must be
> obtained from the librarian.

The Charles Woodward Memorial Room houses one of the finest historical medical and biological libraries in North America. In

Canada it is second only to the Osler Library (which regrettably we have not seen) at McGill University in Montreal.

The library is divided into two parts, the working historical biomedical library on the ground floor, and above on the balcony is a superb collection of very rare and valuable biomedical books. On the ground floor, there are also very fine tapestries showing the history of medicine and other beautiful portraits, busts etc. From time to time there are special exhibits on various aspects of biomedical history. This library should not be missed by anyone going to Vancouver.

VICTORIA

This is the capital city of British Columbia located on Vancouver Island and a very pleasant ferry ride from Vancouver.

The British Columbia Provincial Museum
Belleville and Government Streets
Victoria, B.C.

Opening hours:
>Daily, 10.00 - 17.30
>No charge for admission.

This museum is primarily devoted to science and technology (not medicine), but we mention it here simply because it is large, excellent and very new. They have used modern techniques in all their displays, principally of biology and Indian anthropology. We cannot speak too highly of it. It is one of the best in the world.

INDEX

Académie de Medécine, 128
Académie National des Sciences, 128
Aldershot, 3
Allgemeines Krankenhaus, 187
Altenheim Stammhaus, 148
American Museum of Natural History, 213
Anaesthesia , 31, 67, 207, 209
Anatomisches Museum, 178
Anatomy Museum, 47
Anatomy Theatre, 146, 171, 204
Anthrax, 106, 140
Antiseptic techniques, 42
Antitoxins, 143, 149
Apothecaries, 145
Apothecary Shop, 219
Apotheken Museum, 145
Arbois, 103
Ardingly, 6
Ashford, 8
Augustinian Monastery, 189
Austria, 183

Bacteriology, 140
Banks, Sir Joseph, 51
Banting, Sir Frederick, **222**
Basel, 177
Beaumont, William, **211**
Beaune, 107
Becquerel, Henri, 121, **124**
Behring, Emil von, **149**
Behringwerke und Institut, 149
Belleval, Pierre Richer de, **112**
Berggasse 19, Vienna, 185
Berkeley, 8
Bernard, Claude, 116, 117, 135, **136**
Best, Charles, **223**
Bethesda, 219
Biblioteca Pinale, 172
Bibliothéque de Musée National d'Histoire Naturelle, 127
Bibliothèque National, 131
Bibliothèque Saint Geneviéve, 117
Bionomial nomenclature, 202
Blood, circulation of, 38
Bo, 170
Boston, 206

Botanical Garden of Leiden, 198
Botany Department, Cambridge, 18
Britain, 3
British Columbia Provincial Museum, 226
British Dental Association, 64
British Library, 83
British Museum, 83
British Museum of Natural History, 59
British Society of Immunology, 11
Broadstone, 12
Brno, 188
Brompton Cemetery, 82
Budapest, 192
Buffon, Comte George Louis de, **125**
Bullfinch Building, 209

Calcar, Jan Stephan van, 169
Cambridge, 14
Cambridge University Main Library, 21
Canada, 221
Carolinia Rediviva, 203
Canterbury, 22
Cathedral of Uppsala, 204
Cell theory, 124, **153**
Central Cemetery of Brno, 191
Chain, Sir Ernst, 79
Chantry, 9, 11
Charite Hospital, 143
Charles H. Best Institute, 223
Charles Woodward Memorial Room, 225
Chemotherapy, 144
Chiesa di Santa Croce, 164
Childbed fever, 193
Chloroform, 30, 67
Cholera, 67, 101, 141
Christ's College, Cambridge, 16
Church of St. Margaret of Antioch, 29
Cimetière du Père-Lachaise, 135
Classification, 202
Claude Bernard House, 117
Clausthal-Zellerfeld, 139
Claydon House, 89
Cleveland, 210
Collège de France, 116

227

College of Physicians of Philadelphia, 216
Collip, J.B., 222
Colonial Williamsburg, 219
Conservatoire National des Arts et Métiers, 134
Corpus Christi College, Cambridge, 16
Cowpox, 9
Crick, Francis, **18**
Crystallography, 104
Curie, Irène, 121
Curie, Marie, **120**
Curie, Pierre, **120**
Cuvier, George, **126**
Czechoslovakia, 188

Darwin, Charles, **23**
Darwin College, Cambridge, 17
Dental Museum, 65
Deutsches Medizinhistorisches Museum, 146
Deutsches Museum, 152
Deutsches Röntgen-Museum, 155
Diabetes, 221
Diakoniewerk Kaiserswerth, 148
Digestion, 211
Diptheria, 150
Dohrn, Felix Anton, 166
Dôle, 108
Domkyrkan, 204
Downe, 23
Down House, 23

East Kilbride, 26
East Wellow, 28
École Dentaire de Paris, 130
École Normale Supérieure, 118
École Supérieure de Physique et de Chimie Industrielles de la Ville de Paris, 120
Edinburgh, 29
Ehrlich, Paul, **143**, 149
Ether Dome, 209
Evolution, 23, 124
Experimental physiology, 137

Faculté de Medecine, Montpellier, 110
Faculté de Médecine, Paris, 129
Fauchard, Pierre, **130**
Federal Republic of Germany, 139
Fermentation, 105

Fleming, Sir Alexander, **78**, 82
Florence, 161
Florey, Sir Howard, 79
Folkestone, 38
France, 102
Frankfurt-am-Main, 142
Freud, Anna, 85
Freud Museum, 85
Freud, Sigmund, 85, **185**

Galileo Galilei, 163, 168, **174**
General Museum, Kew, 57
Genetic Garden, 92
Genetics, 189
Geneva, 179
Geological Museum, 62
Germany, West, 139
Germ theory, 105
Giardino Botanico, 173
Glascow, 41
Glasgow Botanic Gardens, 47
Glasgow Royal Infirmary, 42
Gonville and Caius College, Cambridge, 15
Gosport, 48
Gustavianum, 204
Guy's Hospital, 76

Hales, Stephen, 16, **95**
Hampstead Cemetery, 86
Harvard University, 206
Harvey Chapel, 50
Harvey, William, 15, 22, **38**, 171
Haslar, 48
Hauptpost, Neuss, 155
Heidelberg, 144
Heidelberger Schloss, 145
Hematology, 143
Hempstead, 49
Herbarium, Kew, 54
Herb Garden, Philadelphia, 216
Holland, 195
Hooke, Robert, 61, 92
Hooker, Sir Joseph Dalton, **52**
Hooker, Sir William Jackson, 47, **52**
Hôtel de Ville, Beaune, 108
Hôtel Dieu, Beaune, 107
Hôtel Dieu, Paris, 134
Howard Dittrick Museum, 210
Hungary, 192
Hunterian Museum, London, 70
Hunter, John, 26, **71**

Hunter Museum, East Kilbride, 27
Hunter, William, **27**, 46

Immunology, 143
Ingolstadt, 146
Institut für Geschichte der Medizin
    der Universität Wein, 183
Instituto e Museo Storia della
    Scienza, 162
Institut Pasteur, 132
Insulin, 221
Ionizing radiation, 125
Isomerism, 104
Italy, 160

Jardin des Plantes, 112
Jefferson, President Thomas, 11,
    218
Jenner, Edward, **9**
Jenner Museum, 9
John Snow Public House, 66
Josephinum, 183
Jules-Etienne Marey Museum, 108

Kaiserswerth, 147
Kew, 50
King's School, Canterbury, 22
Koch, Robert, **140**, 149

Lamark, Le Chevalier Jean
    Baptiste de, **123**
Lavoisier, Antoine Laurent, **134**
Leeuwenhoek, Antoni van, **196**
Leiden, 195
Library of Congress, 218
Linnaeus, Carl, 63, 199, 200, **201**
Linnaeus' Hammarby, 204
Linnean Society of London, 63
Linnémuseet, 202
Lister, Joseph Lord, **42**, 49, 71
London, 58
Long, Crawford Williamson, **208**
Lund, 199
Lymph system, 204

Mackinac Island, 211
Macleod, John James, **222**
Maer, 88
Main Botanic Gardens, Oxford, 91
Maison Familiale de Pasteur, 103
Maison Natale de Bernard, 138
Maison Natale de Pasteur, 109

Malmö, 199
Marbach, 149
Marburg/Lahn, 148
Marianne North Gallery, 57
Massachusettes General Hospital,
    207
Mechanistic theory of life, 154
Medical Museum, Haslar, 48
Medizinhistorisches Museum, 180
Mendel, Gregor, **189**
Mendelianum, 189
Mendel Museum, 189
Microorganisms, 196
Microscopes, 61, 197
Middle Claydon, 89
Montpellier, 109
Morton, William Thomas, **208**
Mount, The, 94
Munich, 151
Musée Claude Bernard, 136
Musée d'Histoire des Sciences, 179
Musée d'Histoire de la Medécine,
    118
Musée Fauchard et Bibliothéque, 130
Musée Louis Pasteur, Arbois, 103
Musée National d'Histoire Naturelle,
    122
Musée Pasteur, Paris, 132
Museo Zoologica La Specola, 165
Museum Boerhaave, 195
Museum of the History of Science, 91
Mutter Medical Museum, 216

Naples, 166
National Library of Medicine, 219
National Museum of History and
    Technology, 217
Neuss, 153
New York, 213
New York Academy of Medicine, 214
Nightingale, Florence, 29, **73**, 89,
    148
North, Marianne, 57

Oeffnungzeit Museum, 180
Old Cavendish Laboratory, 18
Old Infirmary of Edinburgh and
    Surgeons Hall, 35
Old St Thomas' Hospital Operating
    Theatre, 76
Ontario Science Center, 225
Operating Amphitheatre, 215

Ospedale di Pediatria, 164
Ospedale di Santa Maria Nuova, 164
Oxford, 90
Oxford University, 90
Oxford University Museum, 93

Padua, 168
Palazzo del Bo, 170
Paris, 114
Parish Church of St Anne, 58
Parish Church of St Mary, 97
Parish Church of St Peter, 88
Pasteur Institute, 132
Pasteur, Louis, **103**, 108, 119, 132
Paul-Ehrlich-Institut, 142
Penicillin, 78
Pennsylvania Hospital, 215
Philadelphia, 214
Physikal Institut, 158
Pine Building, 215
Pisa, 173
Psychoanalysis, 185
Puerperal fever, 193

Queen Alexandra's Royal Army
    Nursing Corps Museum, 6

Radioactivity, 125
Rashults Södergard, 200
Remscheid-Lennep, 155
Robert Koch House, 142
Röntgen rays, 156
Röntgen, Wilhelm Conrad, **156**, 158
Rose Garden, Oxford, 91
Rothschild, Lord, 99
Royal Army Dental Corps Museum, 4
Royal Army Medical Corps Historical
    Museum, 5
Royal Botanic Garden of Edinburgh,
    37
Royal Botanic Gardens, Kew, 50
Royal College of Physicians, 65
Royal College of Physicians and
    Surgeons of Glasgow, 45
Royal College of Physicians of
    London, 65
Royal College of Physicians of
    Edinburgh, 37
Royal College of Surgeons of
    Edinburgh, 35
Royal College of Surgeons of
    England, 70

Royal Horticultural Society, 86
Royal Horticultural Society's Gardens
    at Wisley, 100
Royal Infirmary of Edinburgh, 34
Royal Naval Hospital, 48
Royal Society of Edinburgh, 36
Royal Society of London, 68
Rudbeck, Olof, 204

Salvarsan, 144
Schleiden, Mathias, **153**
Schwann, Theodor, **154**
Science Museum, 61
Semmelweis, Ignác, **193**
Semmelweis Medical Historical
    Museum, 193
Serum Institut, 143
Shrewsbury, 94
Sigmund Freud Haus, 185
Simpson, Sir James Young, **30**
Sir James Young Simpson Museum,
    30
Smallpox, 9
Smithsonian Institution, 217
Snow, John, **66**, 82, 101
Sorbonne, 115
Spirochaetes, 144
Stazione Zoologica di Napoli, 166
Stenbrohult, 200
Stereochemistry, 104
Sterilizing, 141
St Andrew's Church, 50
St Julien-en-Beaujolais, 136
St Mary's Hospital Medical School,
    78
St Paul's Cathedral, 82
St Thomas' Hospital, 72
Sulphuric Ether, 207
Sweden, 199
Switzerland, 177
Systematic Garden, 56

Teddington, 95
Tetanus, 150
Thomas Fisher Rare Book Library,
    224
Trephining, 220
Tring, 98
Tring Zoological Museum, 99
Trinity College, Cambridge, 16
Tuberculosis, 141

United States of America, 206
University Botanic Garden,
    Cambridge, 20
Università degli Studi di Padova, 168
Università di Pisa, 174
Universität München, 151
Universität der Wien, 187
Universität Zürich, 180
University of British Columbia, 225
University of Edinburgh, 33
University of Florence, 161
University of Glascow, 46
University of Heidelberg,145
University of Leiden, 195
University of Montpellier, 110
University of Paris, 114
University of Toronto, 222
University of Uppsala, 203
University of Würzburg, 158
Uppsala, 201

Vancouver, 225
Vesalius, Andreas, **168**, 177
Victoria, 226
Vienna, 183
Vienna General Hospital, 187
Viking Hotel, 101
Villa Comunale, 166
Virus, attenuation of, 106

Wakehurst Place Gardens, 7
Wallace, Alfred Russel, **12**
Warren, John Collins, 208
Wars of Religion, 110
Washington, 216
Watson, James, **19**
Wellcome Institute of the History of
    Medicine, 69
Wellcome Museum of the History of
    Medicine, 61
Wellcome, Sir Henry, 61, 69
Wells, Horace, **208**
Westminster Abbey, 81
William Beaumont Memorial Building,
    212
William Boyd Library and Medical
    Museum, 224
Williamsburg, 219
Wipple Museum of the History of
    Science, 20
Wisley, 100
Würzburg, 158

X-rays, 155, 158

York, 101

Zoology Department and Museum,
    Cambridge, 17
Zoology Museum, Glascow, 46
Zürich, 180